# 9B & 9BF

# CLERGET
*Patent*

# AERO ENGINES

*Instructions and*
*List of Parts*

*Manufacturers and Sole Licensees for the British Empire:*

## GWYNNES LTD.

HAMMERSMITH IRON WORKS, HAMMERSMITH, W.6.
& CHURCH WHARF, CHISWICK, W.4.

### LONDON.

Telegrams:
"GWYNNES, LONDON."

Telephone:
1910 HAMMERSMITH

# Introduction

Founded in 1911, the firm of *Clerget-Blin & Cie* was the second of the three French firms which developed the rotary aero engine, the other two being *Gnôme* and *La Rhone*.

During the pioneering days of aviation the rotary engine had the great attraction of a high power to weight ratio and many early records were set using them. The outbreak of World War I resulted in considerable development in aero engines in general, but this high power to weight ratio resulted in rotary engines being extensively used in fighter or 'scout' aircraft where speed and manoeuverability were major requirements.

Demand for the French rotary engines reached such a level during the war that all three firms reached licensing agreements with British manufacturers - in the case of *Clerget* with *Gwynnes Ltd.* who published the manual reproduced here, probably in 1917.

*Clerget* engines were perhaps the best designed of the three makes and were well regarded by pilots and fitters alike. *Clerget* were the only one of the French companies to introduce an engine which came near to developing 200 bhp, but the 9B and 9BF engines covered here were of lesser power, developing 134 bhp at normal revolutions, although this was power enough to make the SOPWITH CAMEL, to which they were fitted, the most successful fighter/scout aircraft of the war.

This manual would have been intended for use by maintenance personnel and the detail, down to the 'nuts & bolts', gives a fascinating insight into the engineering of one of the pre-eminent aircraft engine designs of World War I.

The Publisher acknowledges, with considerable thanks, the help of Mr. Geoff Willis in the publication of this book.

---

Originally published c 1917 by Wynnes Ltd., Hammersmith, London

© this edition - Camden Miniature Steam Services 2001. All rights reserved.

British Library Cataloguing-in-Publication-Data: a catalogue record of this book is held by the British library.

ISBN 0-9536523-1-9

Published in Great Britain by: Camden Miniature Steam Services, Barrow Farm, Rode, Frome, Somerset. BA11 6PS

*Camden* stock one of the widest selections of engineering, technical and transportation books to be found. Write to them at the above address for a copy of their latest Booklist.

Printed by Salisbury Printing Company Limited

# CLERGET

*PATENT*

# AERO ENGINES

## 9B — 130-HORSE
## 9BF — 150-HORSE

*1917*

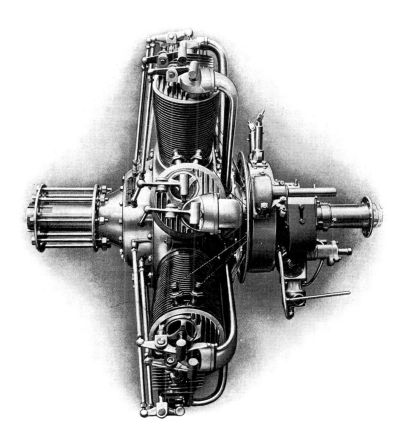

| | | | | |
|---|---|---|---|---|
| **No. *of* CYLINDERS** | ... | *Nine* | SPEED ...    ... | *1250 R.P.M.* |
| **BORE 9B & 9BF** | | *120 m/m*<br>(4¾ in. bare) | **WEIGHT** including | |
| **STROKE—9B** ... | | *160 m/m*<br>(6 5/16 in. bare) | oil pump, air pump | |
| **STROKE—9BF** ... | | *172 m/m*<br>(6¾ in. full) | and two magnetos | *181 Kilos*<br>(400 lbs.) |

# CLERGET PATENT AERO ENGINES.
## 9B—130 H.P. & 9BF—150 H.P.

### LIST OF ILLUSTRATIONS.

### CONTENTS.

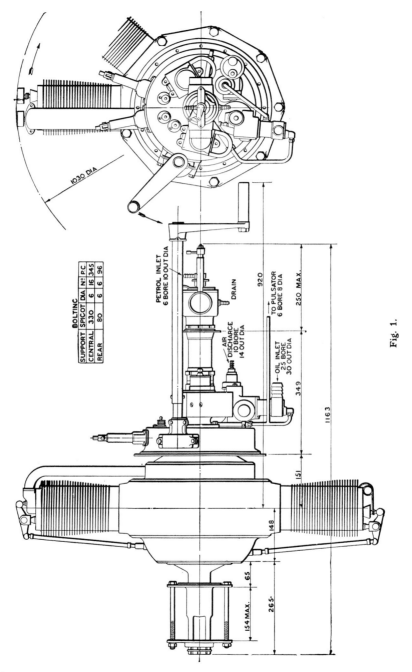

Fig. 1.

| BOLTING | | | |
|---|---|---|---|
| SUPPORT | SPIGOT DIA | Nº | P.C. |
| CENTRAL | 330 | 6 | 16 345 |
| REAR | 80 | 6 | 6 96 |

1030 DIA

PETROL INLET
6 BORE 10 OUT DIA

DRAIN

AIR DISCHARGE
10 BORE
14 OUT DIA

TO PULSATOR
6 BORE 8 DIA

OIL INLET
25 BORE
30 OUT DIA

920

250 MAX.

349

1163

151

148

65

265·

154 MAX.

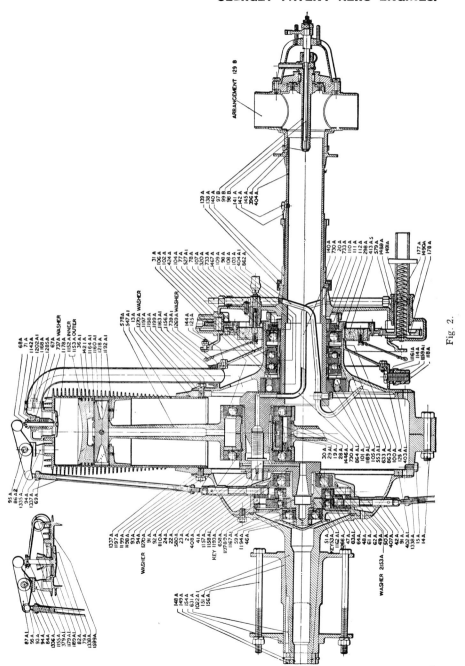

Fig. 2.

5

# GENERAL DESCRIPTION.

A clear idea of the construction of the engine will be obtained if the sectional drawings, Figs. 2 and 3, and the smaller illustrations are referred to while reading the following description.

## VALVE DRIVING GEAR.

This is a distinctive feature of the engine. The inlet and exhaust valves are driven independently by two eccentrics, which are securely fixed to an extension of the short crankshaft (maneton).

For the sake of clearness, the action of the inlet valve gear only is described below, although the description applies equally to the exhaust valve gear.

A cam ball bearing 47A (Fig. 3) is mounted on the inlet eccentric ; the outer race of the bearing forms a 16-toothed wheel which gears into the 18-toothed gear ring 49A, keyed concentrically to the inner surface of the distribution box 580A. Four equally spaced teeth on the outer race of the cam ball bearing are extended the whole width of the bearing, forming cams so arranged that they lift each of the 9 well-guided tappets, 408A, at equal intervals of time, once in every two revolutions of the engine. The motion of the tappet is transmitted, through the ball-ended push rod 1337A, to the outer end of the rocking lever (Fig. 2) which is carried in a bracket screwed into the head of the cylinder, causing the inner end of lever to press on the end of the valve spindle, thus opening the valve. As the cam falls away from the tappet the valve is closed by a spring. The closing is assisted by centrifugal force, and the valve remains securely closed until another cam on the outer race of the ball bearing again lifts the tappet, which happens regularly once in every two revolutions of the engine.

The valve driving gear is of the circular type, therefore the angle formed at the centre of the shaft between a tappet when its valve is just opening and the centre of the eccentric, is always equal to the angle between the same tappet when its valve is just closing and the same eccentric centre.

The rocking lever oscillates upon a suitably shaped hardened steel fulcrum fixed in the lever bracket. The hole in the centre of the lever is made oval, to allow for the oscillation, and has a slight groove for the fulcrum edge to work in.

## INLET AND EXHAUST VALVES.

Every cylinder is provided with one inlet and one exhaust valve.

Each valve is mounted upon a fixed seat screwed into the head of the cylinder, and is guided by the valve spindle passing through an extension of the valve seat (Fig. 2) ; a spring passed over the valve spindle presses against this extension, and the spring is held in compression by a shrouded cap, fixed near the end of the valve spindle by means of a pin stop.

The inlet valve seat is continuous with an inlet chamber (at the back of the valve) and has an oval opening and facing to joint at the top end of the oval induction tube, through which the air and petrol mixture is drawn from the crank case into the cylinder during the charging stroke. The inlet valve is flat on its seat.

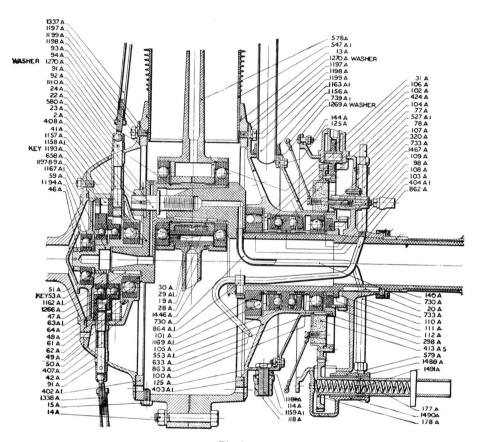

Fig. 3.

*GENERAL DESCRIPTION—(Continued).*

The exhaust valve is coned to its seat, and, when open, discharges directly into the air.

The valves and seats can be removed bodily from the cylinders by unscrewing the valve seats, but when this is done the valves should be re-ground to their seats after seats have been re-fixed in the cylinders.

## CYLINDERS, PISTONS and CONNECTING RODS.

Each cylinder has a collar on its outer surface which is held by a recess in the crank casing, to which it is carefully fitted before the halves of the casing are bolted together and is registered in position by the dowel stop 13A (Fig. 3).

The pistons are of aluminium-copper alloy having phosphor bronze bushes driven in. They are provided with 3 C.I. cut rings, in addition to double obturator rings made of special silver alloy.

Each piston drives an independent connecting rod. One of these, called the master rod, is continuous with a banjo at the crank end ; this rod holds all the pistons in their correct relative positions. The remaining 8 rods are hinged to the banjo by removable pins. All the rods are hollow, and the journals at the piston end are lubricated centrifugally through the hollow centre of the rods.

## CRANKSHAFT and SUPPORTS.

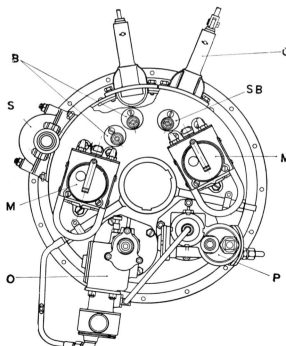

The crankshaft is coned and keyed for attachment to the central support, and is held in position by a locked sleeve nut. The crankshaft is always fixed with the crank-pin on the top centre.

The details for drawing the crankshaft out of the central support are clearly shown in Fig. 3.

The butting ends of the central support, 527A.1. and the sleeve nut, 140A, are provided with narrow collars, over which two half-rings, 138A, are loosely fitted; the half rings are held in place by a specially sawn steel ring, 139A. When the sleeve nut is slacked back, the half-rings are drawn back with

Fig. 4. Central Support Mountings.

it until their rear collar is pressing against the collar on the sleeve nut and their front collar against the collar on the central support boss ; if the nut is screwed further back the central support will be drawn along with it, and freed from the cone to which it is bedded.

In addition to the central support, the engine is fitted with a rear support which is held in position laterally by a nut, but it is not keyed to prevent turning.

Should engines be mounted with a long or medium nose piece, a front support containing a ball bearing must always be fitted.

## MOUNTINGS on CENTRAL SUPPORT.

The auxiliaries mounted on the back of the central support may include (Fig. 4) :—

S—Hand starter.

G—Gun interrupter gear.

M—Magnetos, two in number.

O—Oil pump.

P—Petrol air-pressure pump.

B—Brush holders, three in number.

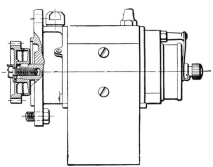

One of these, marked (S.B.) in the illustration, is used as a starting brush holder.

The magneto supplied is of the A.D.S. type, and is fitted with a pinion and crown wheel (Fig. 5). The pinion is driven by the main driving wheel, 112A.

Fig. 5.   Magneto.

Ratio—9 revs. to 4 revs. of engine.
2 sparks per rev. of magneto.
9 sparks to 2 revs. of engine.

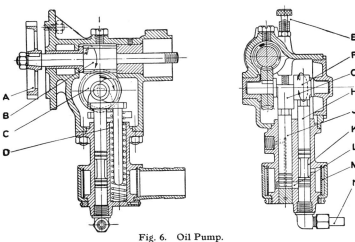

Fig. 6.   Oil Pump.

**CLERGET PATENT AERO ENGINES**

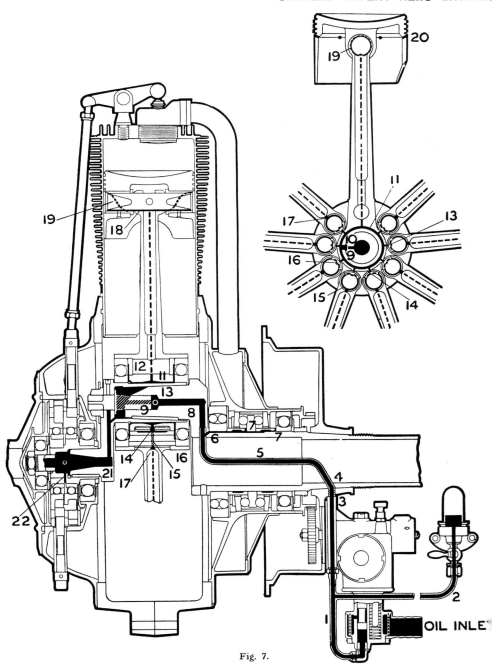

Fig. 7.

10

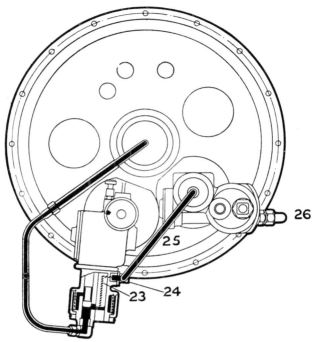

# — OILING SYSTEM —

## MAIN SUPPLY

| | | M/M |
|---|---|---|
| 1 | OIL PIPE, MAIN TO ENGINE | 6 BORE 8 OUT |
| 2 | BRANCH PIPE TO PULSATOR | 6 BORE 8 OUT |
| 3 | CONNECTION ON CENTRAL SUPPORT | 5 BORE |
| 4 | MATCHING HOLE IN CRANKSHAFT | 6 DIA |
| 5 | OIL TUBE INSIDE CRANKSHAFT | 6 BORE 8 OUT |

## THRUST & MAIN BEARINGS

| | | |
|---|---|---|
| 6 | HOLE IN NECK OF CRANK, WITH GROOVE UNDER BALL RACES | 2 DIA |
| 7 | GROOVES ON REAR ENDS OF THRUST DISTANCE PIECES | |

## CON. ROD BEARINGS

| | | |
|---|---|---|
| 8 | HOLE DRILLED IN CRANKWEB & PIN | 6 & 8 DIA |
| 9 | HOLE & SLOT IN CRANKPIN | 4 DIA |
| 10 | MATCHING HOLE IN MANETON CRANK | 5 DIA |
| 11 | ANNULAR SPACE IN MASTER ROD | |
| 12 | CLEARANCE BEHIND BALL BEARINGS | |
| 13 | 9 HOLES IN MASTER ROD BIG END | 2·5 DIA & 2·7 DIA |
| 14 | SLOT OPENINGS IN AUXILIARY CON. ROD BIG ENDS & BUSHES | |

| | | M/M |
|---|---|---|
| 15 | GROOVE INSIDE EACH BIG END BUSH | |
| 16 | GROOVE ON EACH WRIST PIN | |
| 17 | HOLE THROUGH EACH BIG END BUSH INTO HOLLOW CON. ROD | 3 DIA |
| 18 | GROOVE ALONG EACH GUDGEON PIN | |
| 19 | SPIRAL GROOVE INSIDE EACH PISTON BUSH | |
| 20 | 6 HOLES IN PISTON, OIL DRAINAGE | 3 DIA |

## DISTRIBUTION BOX

| | | |
|---|---|---|
| 21 | CLEARWAY THROUGH MANETON INTO EXTENSION SHAFT | 3 DIA |
| 22 | TWO HOLES DRILLED IN EXT. SHAFT | 2 DIA |

## AIR PUMP

| | | |
|---|---|---|
| 23 | HOLE THROUGH OIL PUMP PLUNGER | 1 DIA |
| 24 | NIPPLE IN BOSS ON OIL PUMP | |
| 25 | OIL PIPE TO AIR PUMP | 6 BORE 8 OUT |
| 26 | DRAIN FROM AIR PUMP | |

Fig. 8.

The oil pump (Fig. 6) is driven by its pinion A through the worm gear BC ; two cams, FG, formed on the worm shaft acting against the springs D, force the regulating plunger J and the valve plunger H to descend, and the springs in their turn force the plungers upwards as the cams pass from their lowest position. The action of the pump is as follows :—

The oil flows into the inlet chamber M, through the gauze strainer, and into the annular space K round the reduced portion of the valve plunger ; the valve plunger descends, and the regulating plunger ascends, drawing the oil after it through the opening L ; the valve plunger then ascends, and the regulating plunger descends, forcing the oil back through the opening into the space under the valve plunger, and from there into the oil supply pipe N. This pump must not be driven in the opposite direction to that for which it is designed ; the action would be reversed. The oiling system may be followed on Figs. 7 and 8.

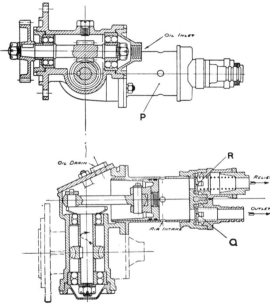

Fig. 9. Air Pump.

The petrol air pressure pump (Fig. 9) is also driven by its pinion, and through worm gear. This pump has no suction valve, the air being admitted through the holes P in the barrel when the plunger is near the inward end of its stroke. The delivery valve Q is of the plate type and of ample size. The pump, in addition to supplying the air required to displace the petrol used, will deliver an ample margin to allow for reasonable accidental leakage from the delivery pipe or petrol tank, and to deal with this excess air an adjustable relief valve R is provided. The air pump is lubricated by a U pipe from the oil pump barrel, through which a small oil supply is arranged.

The hand starting gear (Fig. 4) is attached to the side of the central support. The pinion of the starting gear has helical teeth ; normally this pinion is held clear of the distribution plate by a strong spiral spring, but when in use, the pinion is pressed forward to engage with teeth formed on the rim of the distribution plate. The hand crank is turned anti-clockwise to start the engine, and directly the engine starts, the pinion is forced out of gear and clear of the distribution plate by its helical teeth.

The starting gear is also illustrated at the bottom of Fig. 3.

*GENERAL DESCRIPTION—(Continued).*

## CARBURETTOR.

The carburettor, screwed on the end of the crankshaft, is provided with two levers ; the inner and larger governs both the air and petrol supply, and the outer and smaller adjusts the petrol to suit altitude.

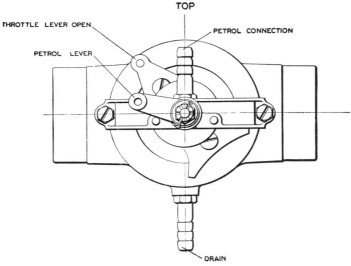

Fig. 10.   Carburettor Setting.

For preliminary setting, turn the throttle lever to the extreme left (open), and the petrol lever to the same position as shown on Fig. 10 ; with the levers in these positions the central needle should project ·5m/m beyond the extreme end of the nozzle.   The crown clutch on the petrol lever enables this adjustment to be made.

Final adjustment is made during test of the engine.   With the crown clutch removed, and throttle lever set at full open, the petrol needle is turned right-hand motion till engine begins to miss fire, and with needle in this position the petrol lever is fixed by the crown clutch at mid-position.

An alternative method which gives good running conditions is to remove crown clutch, set throttle lever at full open, and adjust petrol needle to obtain good running conditions at 1200 to 1250 R.P.M.; with the petrol needle in this position the petrol lever is fixed at its extreme position to the left (Fig. 10).   This gives the maximum petrol opening allowable at the needle, and any movement of the petrol lever, when thus adjusted and fixed by crown clutch, must be to the right, thus reducing the petrol area at the needle end. By this means the necessary control over petrol at higher altitudes is obtained, and the danger of flooding is reduced to a minimum.

The type of carburettor has recently been altered and in future engines will be supplied fitted with a special type of Bloc-tube Carburettor, with air inlet branches of stream-line shape.

# DIRECTIONS FOR OPENING UP ENGINE.

## DISMOUNTING.

Unscrew the carburettor from the end of the crankshaft and the nut from the back of rear support ; draw off the air screw ; it should be noted that the engine revolves in a contra-clockwise direction when looking on engine from air-screw end.

## LOCKING DEVICES.

Carefully note all spring washers, wire stops and other locking devices.

## REMOVAL OF CONNECTING RODS AND PISTONS.

Remove distribution box. (See directions under " Opening up Distribution Box.")

Remove locking washer from maneton nut.

Unscrew maneton screw by its nut (R.H. thread), drawing maneton from its crank ; this should bring the front connecting rod ball bearing with it.

To assist in starting this ball bearing, tap round big end of master rod with chock of hard wood.

The maneton nut is not to be removed from the screw but may be considered as part of it.

Note that the master rod is in No. 1 cylinder.

Place No. 2 cylinder between the horizontal and 30 degs. from the bottom centre.

Draw out Nos. 2 and 3 wrist pins by a special screw tool.

Give quarter turn to rod and piston, bringing cut-away portion to front, and carefully remove Nos. 2 and 3 rods with pistons attached.

Proceed in same way with remainder, removing each rod before the next pin is drawn out, leaving No. 1 rod and piston to the last.

When withdrawing master rod No. 1 from crankpin, place No. 1 cylinder in horizontal position and slightly move engine backward and forward to find easiest position for angling the rod end over the cut-away portion of crankpin. It must not be forced.

Erection marks should be noted and matched when re-assembling.

## OPENING UP DISTRIBUTION BOX.

Remove air screw shaft.

Draw out centring plate.

Remove split pin and unscrew front nut from extension shaft.

Remove wire rings from rocking lever pins and press out the pins.

Swing levers clear of brackets, *but do not revolve the engine till you have inserted clips under ball caps of tappets.* This is important, and disregard of this precaution may result in the bending of the tappets.

Remove nuts and spring washers from studs connecting distribution box to crankcase.

Screw special withdrawing screw on to the end of extension shaft.

Place tripod over same, taking a bearing on three of the cylinder flanges of crankcase.

Screw on nut and continue to turn till distribution box and contents are free from crankcase and maneton.

Place distribution box carefully on a bench and proceed as follows :—

Draw off front ball bearing.

Remove bevel distance washer.

(Note that bevel side is upwards towards ball bearing).

Draw off front (exhaust) eccentric with cam ball bearing attached.

Draw out exhaust cam driving ring.

Turn distribution box up on edge and remove the ring stop and rear nut from inner end of extension shaft.

The extension shaft can now be pressed out from the front of the case with the rear (inlet) eccentric and cam ball bearing attached.

Drive out taper pins from ball caps and tappets, noting that large end of taper is on the leading side when engine is revolving.

Draw off the ball caps.

Remove tappets from inside of case.

Inlet cam driving ring can now be removed and also the fixed disc under same.

Do not attempt to drive out the bronze tappet guides except to remove damaged ones.

Before removing nut inside of the case that holds ball bearing in place, note the position of ring stop and mark nut and inside of case to ensure matching when re-assembling.

The ring stop can then be removed, the nut unscrewed (R.H. thread) and the ball bearing drawn out from inside of case.

## CENTRAL SUPPORT.

This is coned and keyed to crankshaft and held in place by long sleeve nut screwed on crankshaft and fixed by shaped stop.

Unscrew sleeve nut (R.H. thread).

This draws support off shaft cone by means of internally collared half-rings.

There is no need to remove the special sawn containing ring which is riveted over these half-rings.

When sleeve nut is free from the thread on shaft, engine can be carefully lifted out of the plane and placed rear side up on special erecting frame.

## OPENING UP THRUST GEAR.

Remove nuts and spring washers from studs fixing rear drum to crankcase.

Undo wiring from sparking plugs.

Remove screws holding induction tube flange to inlet valve seat.

Unscrew nuts from bolts holding clamps on flanges at rear drum end of tubes and draw out induction tubes.

Rear drum can now be removed from crankcase.

Remove wire ring and unscrew rear crankshaft nut (R.H. thread) inside of driving wheel.

Before doing so, crankshaft should be carefully held in wood clamps to prevent same from turning.

Carefully tap out crankshaft, which will probably take front or main ball bearing with it.

Remove grub screw from the nut underneath main bearing in gear box and unscrew the nut (R.H. thread).

The following parts can then be drawn out from the front end of the rear drum :—

| *Centred on Shaft.* | | *Centred in Case.* |
|---|---|---|
| Front distance piece (short). | | Front thrust race. |
| | Ball cage. | |
| Central thrust race. | | Central distance piece (thin). |
| | Ball cage. | |
| Rear distance piece (long). | | Rear thrust race. |

When replacing the front (short) distance piece and the rear (long) distance piece, the oil groove at one end of these distance pieces should be placed at the top of the shaft and to the rear.

## TO RELEASE REAR BEARING.

Unscrew the main driving wheel (L.H. thread).

Leather oil ring will come away with the wheel.

Remove distance washer, noting that flat side is against the leather washer.

The rear ball bearing can now be pressed out at the rear end of the rear drum.

## CYLINDERS.

Never remove cylinders from the casing unless it is absolutely necessary to do so in order to replace damaged cylinder.

# DIRECTIONS FOR RE-ASSEMBLING THE ENGINE.

The central support can if desired be re-mounted on the crankshaft without removing any of the mountings attached to it ; guide the key into the keyway, and slide along the shaft until the pinions of the pumps and magnetos are nearly touching the driving wheel ; screw the coupling nut on by hand, making sure that the various pinions engage in the driving wheel. Do not use the coupling spanner till this is the case, or the wheels may be forced face to face, causing damage.

The re-assembly of the pistons, rods and cam gear may be done with the engine either in the aeroplane or resting on the erecting stand, and the directions given for opening up apply equally for assembling, the order for the various operations naturally being reversed.

During re-erection the following points should receive special attention.

## CLEANLINESS.

Make sure that all the working parts are quite clean and well oiled before replacing them in the engine, and before finally closing up squirt as much lubricating oil into the rear drum and distribution box as they will hold.

## LOCKING DEVICES.

In no case should any of the spring washers, split pins and various locking devices be omitted when assembling.

## PISTONS.

The joints of the inner and outer obturator rings should overlap each other by about $1\frac{1}{2}$ inches ; the rings will then be quite pliable. If the joints are placed opposite or nearly opposite, this pliability is partly lost, and the rings are not then so likely to make a good gas-tight joint under running conditions. The pistons must all be fitted with the cut-away edge on the trailing side ; if this is not done they will not clear each other when engine is revolved.

## MASTER AND AUXILIARY CONNECTING RODS.

Press rear bearing into big end before the master rod is entered into engine.

After fitting the master rod in place in cylinder No. 1, next proceed with the pistons and rods for cylinders Nos. 2 and 9. This is advisable to ensure clearance. The remainder can be connected up in any convenient order, but do not replace the last two wrist pins till all the pistons are in their cylinders.

After all the rods and wrist pins are in place, screw on the maneton on which front bearing of big end has previously been placed, and be quite sure *that both* bearings are pressed hard home into their housings and that inner and outer races are linable.

## CAM AND TAPPET GEAR.

Before assembling the cam gear, read instructions under the heading of " Cam Setting."

17

## AIR SCREW AND NOSE PIECE.

In order to avoid undue vibration, the air screw should be truly balanced, and a good fit on the nose piece. Should the engine run with too much vibration, the first opportunity should be taken to ascertain :—

1. Whether the nose piece has been damaged in any way.

2. Whether the fit of air screw hub on the nose piece is good.

3. Whether the flanges of the air screw hub are parallel to each other.

4. Whether the air screw and nose piece run truly and evenly when the engine is turned by hand.

## CARBON BRUSHES.

The carbon brushes should be examined after running as they may be broken, worn, or stuck up in holders ; when replacing, try that they do not press too heavily against the distributor plate. There should be 3m/m clearance at back of carbons for the spring to act.

# ADJUSTMENT.

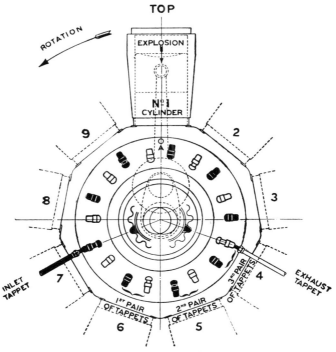

Fig. 11.   Cam Setting.

## CAM SETTING.

Should be done with distribution box removed from the crank casing.

Insert cam gear rear ball bearing and screw on nut inside of case, fixing same with wire ring.

Press home the fixed disc.

Insert the inlet tappets (long) into their guides.

Press in the inlet gear driving ring with distance pegs inwards.

Insert all exhaust tappets (short) in their guides.

Take extension shaft with inlet cam bearing attached and turn the outer race with cam tooth at the extreme throw of the eccentric.

Insert this in distribution box with the extended cam tooth engaging with the inlet tappet No. 7, which will then be held in its extreme outward position.   (Fig. 11).

Turn case up and fix nut at back to hold extension shaft in place, locking same with wire ring.

Before proceeding further, make sure that extension shaft and cam have not shifted from the positions in which they were previously set.

*ADJUSTMENTS—(Continued).*

Press in the exhaust gear driving ring with distance pegs inwards.

Take exhaust eccentric with cam bearing attached and turn the outer race with a cam tooth at the extreme throw of eccentric, that is, in line with keyway.

Count 3 pairs of tappets in contra-clockwise direction from the inlet tappet previously chosen and slide the eccentric on to shaft with the extended cam tooth engaging with the exhaust tappet of the third pair, which will thus be held in its extreme position. This will be No. 4, exhaust tappet.

If the spaces chosen are correct the key in extension shaft will match the keyway in the eccentric.

Place bevelled washer on outer end of extension shaft with bevelled edge outward (toward ball bearing).

Press on ball bearing.

Screw on front nut and fix with stop pin.

If the tappet ball caps are not yet fitted they can now be pressed on ends of tappets and fixed by means of their taper pins. The big end of the taper pins to be arranged on the leading side.

This should be done and the brass clips inserted between the caps and tappet guides before revolving the cam gear.

This is to prevent the possibility of bending tappets.

Before fixing distribution box to crankcase, turn engine with cylinder No. 1, containing master rod, on top centre.

With the eccentrics and cams in positions mentioned above, the stud hole of distribution box between inlet and exhaust tappets No. 1 should then

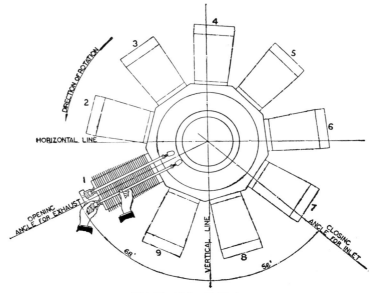

Fig. 12.   Valve Setting.

*ADJUSTMENTS—(Continued).*

be placed on top centre and in this position the gear case should be connected up.

If instructions have been correctly followed the keyway in extension shaft will match the key in maneton end and the distribution box can be pressed into place and connected up with nuts and spring washers.

The cam gear may be set by other tappets if desired ; thus if No. 9 inlet tappet is chosen, the exhaust tappet required will be No. 6, and the cylinder No. 3 should be on top centre before gear case is attached, the stud hole of gear case between No. 3 inlet and exhaust tappets being also placed on top centre.

## VALVE SETTING.

Valves should always be set after gear case has been opened up, and the setting checked before a flight.

The nose piece should be attached before valves are set.

Always set valves in the same order.

Set exhaust valves first, taking the cylinders in their firing sequence, that is, 1, 3, 5, 7, 9, 2, 4, 6, 8.

Place cylinder No. 1 at 68 degs. before the bottom dead centre on the *explosion* stroke. This is the position at which exhaust valve should open.

With the left hand make sure that rocking lever pin is riding truly in the slight recess of the central boss of rocking lever, and with the right hand try that the slack is just taken up.

Slightly revolve engine to make sure of the exact point where this occurs. If too late push rod requires lengthening, or if too early shortening.

Screw the ball end at tappet end in to shorten, or out to lengthen rod.

After adjusting, tighten up back nut and *again try that setting is correct.*

After all the exhaust valves are set, proceed with the inlet valves.

Turn No. 1 cylinder to 56 degs. past the bottom dead centre on the *compression* stroke. This is the position at which the inlet valve should close, and proceed in the same order of cylinders as before.

The opening angle of each of the inlet valves should be carefully noted. This should be 4 degs. before top centre, and in no case should it be allowed to exceed 5 degs. before top dead centre. If the 5 degs. is exceeded the inlet valve setting must be re-adjusted to bring the angle down to that amount.

## VALVE AND MAGNETO SETTING.

| | Opens. | Closes. |
|---|---|---|
| Inlet valve | 4° before top centre. | 56° after bottom centre. |
| Exhaust valve | 68° before bottom centre. | 4° after top centre. |
| Magneto | Gap just opening (test with cigarette paper). | |
| | 22° before end of compression stroke. | |

## ADJUSTING THE MAGNETOS.

The magnetos should be adjusted to give a spark on the compression stroke 22° before the cylinder arrives at the top centre. This adjustment is made by means of the crown wheel which engages with the magneto pinion.

*ADJUSTMENTS—(Continued).*

## ADJUSTING THE AIR SUPPLY TO PETROL TANK.

This is done by screwing the spring cap of the relief valve in or out, as required, and once set, further attention is seldom required.

In case of loss of air pressure, due to pipe or tank leakage, screw down the spring cap until the desired pressure is maintained ; tighten the lock nut after adjusting.

## ADJUSTING THE OIL SUPPLY.

The mill-headed screw E at the top of the oil pump is screwed in to reduce the oil supply, and slackened back to increase it ; tighten the lock nut after adjusting.

## MOUNTING THE ENGINE.

Great care should be taken to have the foundations to which the engine is to be bolted true in all directions ; perfectly linable ; machined faces at right angles to the centre line ; machined faces correct distances apart.

When mounting the engine, try all round the supports with a feeler, and do not attempt to bolt up if there is not a metal-to-metal contact all round.

In the case of engines fitted with long or medium nose pieces, the front of the engine must be supported at all times, whether during assembly or mounting ; do not risk injury by neglecting this.

## PRECAUTIONS BEFORE STARTING.

Test the carbon brushes.

If the engine has been standing for any time, examine and clean the sparking plugs, more particularly those at the bottom of the engine where oil may have accumulated.

Try all nuts and see that stops and spring washers are in place.

Examine the wiring.

See that the working parts of all auxiliaries are well lubricated.

Prime the oil pump.

Turn the engine two or three times, to make sure that everything is running free, and to distribute any oil there may be in the casing.

# GENERAL INFORMATION.

Petrol consumption—·82 pints per E.H.P. hour.

Oil consumption—·12 pints per E.H.P. hour.

Oil pressure from 10 lbs. to 30 lbs. per sq. in., depending upon weather and other conditions.

Lubricating oil—pure castor oil.

## CLEARANCES.

Obturator rings—1·5 m/m gap when just entered in cylinder.
$1\frac{1}{2}$ inches between gaps of inner and outer rings.

Piston rings—1·5 m/m gap when just entered in cylinder.

All rings must sink clear into piston —try with straight edge. Piston ring side clearance—·06 m/m for all rings.

Pistons in cylinders—·65 m/m in the diameter at top of piston.
·55 m/m in the diameter at skirt of piston.

Tappets—about 2 m/m. The valves must *not* be set by the clearance.

Brushes—about 3 m/m for spring to act when brush is on distributor plate.

Gudgeon pins in bushes—·1 m/m in the diameter.

Wrist pins in bushes—·08 m/m in the diameter.

Valve stems in guides—inlet ·1 m/m in the diameter. Exhaust ·25 m/m.

Tappets in guides—·05 m/m in the diameter.

## INCORRECT PLACING OF PARTS.

The following list gives the parts most likely to be incorrectly replaced, and their correct positions :—

Pistons—Cut-away edges all one way—trailing.

Distance washer against leather in gear wheel—Flat side to leather.

Thrust distance pieces on shaft—Long, away from cylinders. Short, towards cylinders. Both with oil groove at top and to the rear.

Gear rings—Inlet enters first, then exhaust. Distance pegs inwards in both rings.

Washer under front ball bearing—Chamfered side towards ball bearing.

Tappets—Long for inlet. Short for exhaust.

Push rods—Short for inlet. Long for exhaust.

Rocking levers—Long for inlet. Short for exhaust.

Taper pins in tappet caps—Big ends of pins lead.

Wiring—Wire up from leading segment in outer ring, and trailing segment in inner ring on distributor to the same cylinder.

Distribution box—Stud hole midway between No. 1 inlet and exhaust tappets goes to the top when No. 1 cylinder is at top. Be careful not to connect up one pitch out.

## PARTS NOT TO BE DISCONNECTED
(unless absolutely necessary).

Cam ball bearings from eccentrics.

Bolts holding casing halves together.

Inlet valve seats from cylinders.

Lever brackets from cylinders.

Tappet guides from gear box.

Ball ends and nuts from cylinder end of push rods.

Ball ends from rocking levers.

Square nut and screw from maneton.

Holding tube and half-rings from long sleeve nut.

Cover from air pump barrel.

## THINGS TO LOOK OUT FOR WHEN OPENING UP ENGINE.

This list is not to be considered as containing all the points that require noting when opening up, as there are a number of such points common to all rotary aeroplane engines which have not been included.

Piston rings—Broken or worn.

Obturator rings—Broken or unevenly worn.

Cylinders—Blueing ; gauge diameter for truth ; if ·1 m/m out of truth fresh cylinder should be fitted.

Inlet valve and seat—Valve fractured at neck ; renew.
     Valve not seating evenly ; re-grind.

Exhaust valve and seat—Valve fractured at neck ; renew.
     Valve not seating evenly ; re-grind.
     Valve stem radius fouling guide ; grind back guide.
     Guide bush broken ; renew.

Valve springs—Loss of tension.

Valve spring locking pins—Bent or worn.

Rocking levers—Sign of fracture under side of arm at weight end ; renew.
     Wear in central hole under fulcrum ; considerable wear is allowable here, but it should be noted.

Connecting rod pins—Signs of heating or undue wear ; indicates shortage of oil, or incorrect alignment.

## STANDARD MARKINGS.

The standard markings of the various parts are shown on Fig. 13.

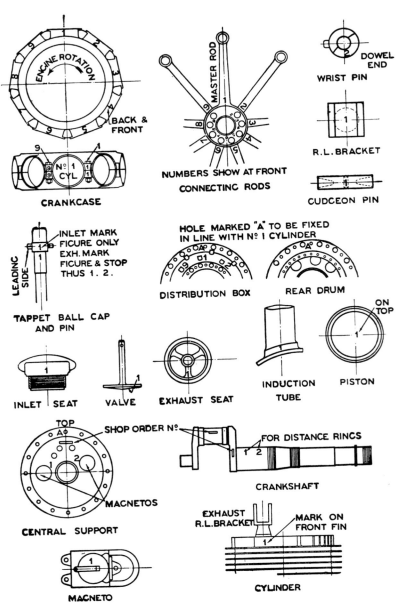

Fig. 13.

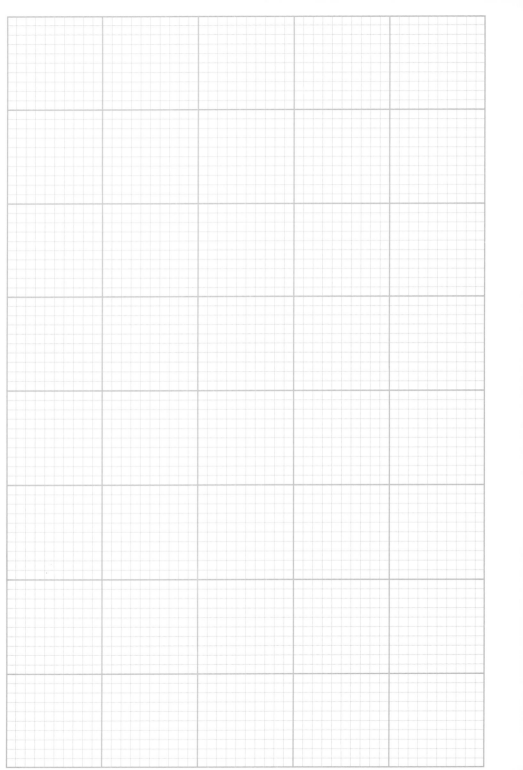

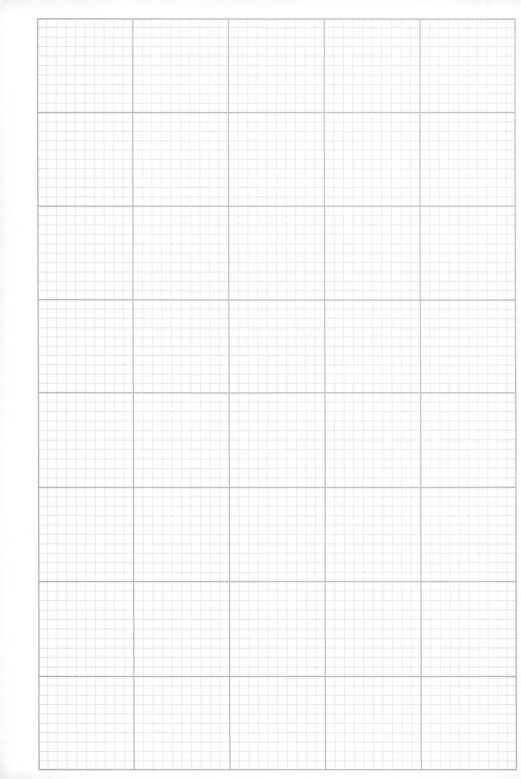

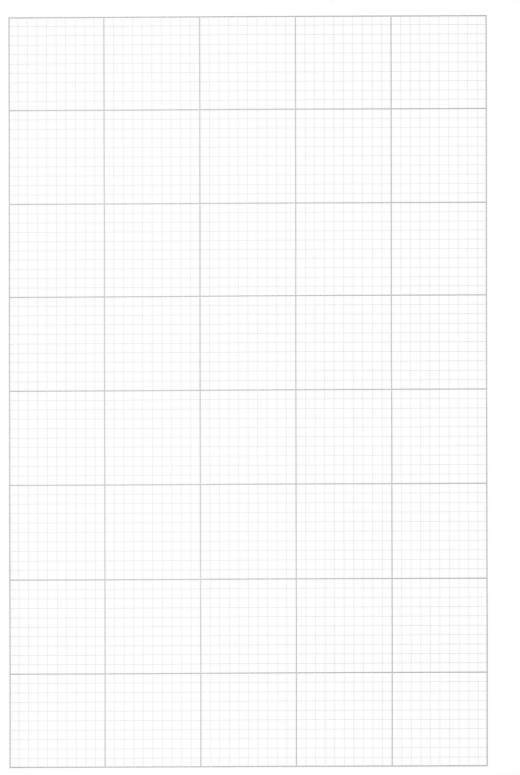

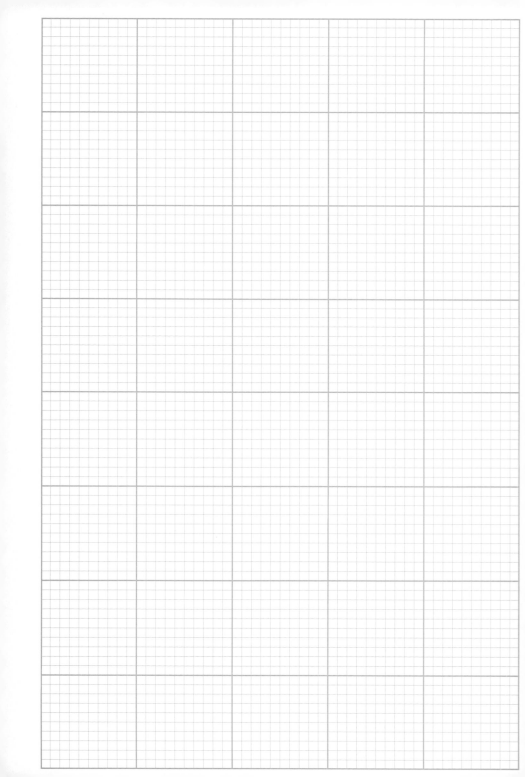

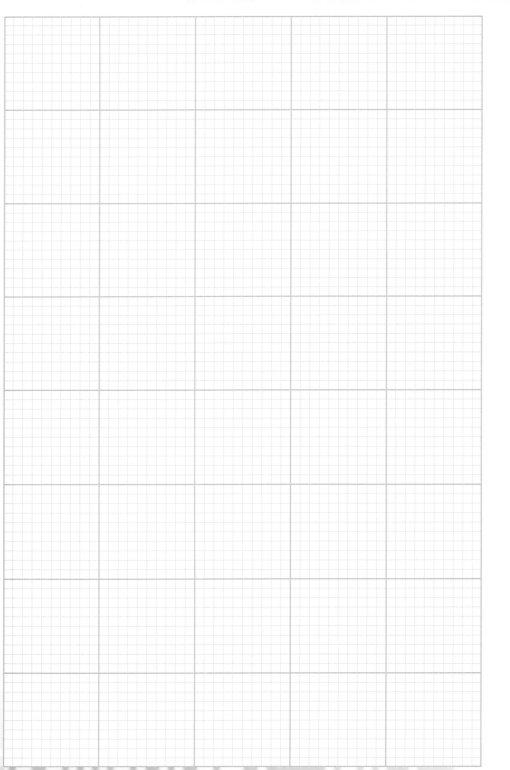

# *Illustrated*
# LIST *of* PARTS
## *with Code-Words*

### *for*

# CLERGET 9B & 9BF

## *Patent*

# AERO ENGINES

❧

The details in the following list are arranged in convenient divisions for reference, and each division is arranged in strict alphabetical order.

The code-words given are in all cases for one item only, and if more than one is wanted, the number required should be added after code-word when ordering.

> Example :—HIGGL indicates *one* cylinder complete with mountings as described for Part No. 2063A.
>
> HIGGL NINE indicates *nine* cylinders complete with mountings as described for Part No. 2063A.

An index—based upon the progressive Part Nos.—has been added at the end of the book.

# CLERGET 9B & 9BF PATENT AERO ENGINES.

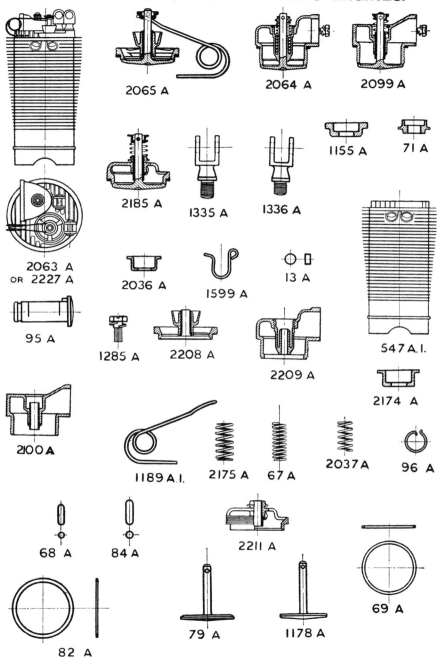

2065 A

2064 A

2099 A

1155 A

71 A

2185 A

1335 A

1336 A

2063 A
OR 2227 A

2036 A

1599 A

13 A

547 A.I.

95 A

1285 A

2208 A

2209 A

2174 A

2100 A

1189 A.I.

2175 A

67 A

2037A

96 A

68 A

84 A

2211 A

69 A

82 A

79 A

1178 A

**GWYNNES LTD., HAMMERSMITH IRON WORKS, LONDON, W.**

# CLERGET 9B & 9BF PATENT AERO ENGINES.

| Part No. | No. per Engine | Description | Code-word for one. |
|---|---|---|---|
| 2063 A | 9 | **CYLINDER,** complete with inlet valve assembly Type A, exhaust valve assembly Type A, inlet lever bracket with fulcrum pin and stop ring, exhaust lever bracket with fulcrum pin and stop ring. | Higgl |
| 2227 A | 9 | **CYLINDER,** as above, but with inlet valve assembly Type B and exhaust valve assembly Type B. | Higha |
| (Type A) 2064 A (Type B) 2099 A | 9 | **INLET VALVE ASSEMBLY,** comprising valve, valve seat, guide bush, spring, spring cap, spring stop pin, seat washer and 2 screws for tube flange. | (Type A) Higns (Type B) Higup |
| (Type A) 2065 A (Type B) 2185 A | 9 | **EXHAUST VALVE ASSEMBLY,** comprising valve, valve seat, guide bush, spring, spring cap, spring stop pin, seat washer (and spring clip, Type A only). | (Type A) Higiz (Type B) Higoa |

## CYLINDER AND VALVE DETAILS.

| Part No. | No. per Engine | Description | | | Code-word for one. |
|---|---|---|---|---|---|
| 1335 A | 9 | Bracket, long, inlet rocking lever | | Steel | Hilly |
| 1336 A | 9 | Bracket, short, exhaust rocking lever | | Steel | Hilog |
| 1155 A | 9 | Cap, spring, exhaust | (A) | Steel | Hilsa |
| 2174 A | 9 | Cap, spring, exhaust | (B) | Steel | Hilpo |
| 71 A | 9 | Cap, spring, inlet | (A) | Steel | Hilte |
| 2036 A | 9 | Cap, spring, inlet | (B) | Steel | Hilum |
| 1599 A | 9 | Clip, spring, exhaust | (A) only | Steel | Himac |
| 547 A. 1 | 9 | Cylinder, 120 m/m dia. | | Steel | Himer |
| 13 A | 9 | Dowel, cylinder to crankcase | | Steel | Himon |
| 95 A | 18 | Pin, fulcrum, exhaust or inlet | | Steel | Himse |
| 1285 A | 18 | Screw, tube flange to inlet seat | | Steel | Himus |
| 2208 A | 9 | Seat, exhaust valve, complete with guide bush | (A) | Steel | Hinam |
| 2211 A | 9 | Seat, exhaust valve, complete with guide bush | (B) | Steel | Hinca |
| 2209 A | 9 | Seat, inlet valve, complete with guide bush | (A) | Steel Cstg. | Hindu |
| 2100 A | 9 | Seat, inlet valve, welded, with guide bush | (B) | Steel | Hinge |
| 1189 A.1 | 9 | Spring, exhaust valve (grasshopper) | (A) | Steel | Hinip |
| 2175 A | 9 | Spring, exhaust valve (spiral) | (B) | Steel | Hinks |
| 67 A | 9 | Spring, inlet valve (spiral) | (A) | Steel | Hinny |
| 2037 A. 1 | 9 | Spring, inlet valve (spiral) | (B) | Steel | Hinto |
| 96 A | 18 | Stop, ring, fulcrum pin | | Steel | Hipoc |
| 84 A | 9 | Stop, spring, exhaust | (A) or (B) | Steel | Hippo |
| 68 A | 9 | Stop, spring, inlet | (A) or (B) | Steel | Hipsh |
| 79 A | 9 | Valve, exhaust (coned seat) | (A) or (B) | Steel | Hiram |
| 1178 A | 9 | Valve, inlet (flat seat) | (A) or (B) | Steel | Hirci |
| 82 A | 9 | Washer, exhaust seat to cylinder | (A) or (B) | Copper— Asbestos | Hired |
| 69 A | 9 | Washer, inlet seat to cylinder (in three grades) | (A) or (B) | Steel | Hirul |

The details listed above are illustrated on opposite page over their respective Part Nos.

# CLERGET 9B & 9BF PATENT AERO ENGINES.

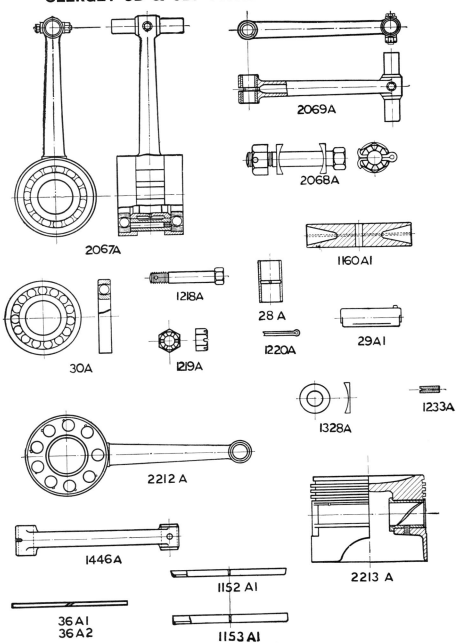

2069A

2068A

2067A

1160A1

1218A

28 A

1220A

29A1

30A

1219A

1233A

1328A

2212 A

1446A

2213 A

1152 A1

36A1
36A2

1153A1

GWYNNES LTD., HAMMERSMITH IRON WORKS, LONDON, W.

# CLERGET 9B & 9BF PATENT AERO ENGINES.

| Part No. | No. per Engine | Description | | Code-word for one. |
|---|---|---|---|---|
| 2067 A | 1 | **MASTER ROD,** with oil plugs, gudgeon pin, gudgeon pin bolt, nut, washers and split pin, 8 wrist pins and stops, and 2 ball bearings. | | Hispa |
| 2069 A | 8 | **AUXILIARY ROD,** with gudgeon pin, gudgeon pin bolt, nut, washers and split pin, and bush and grub screw for wrist pin. | | Hissi |
| 2068 A | 9 | **GUDGEON PIN BOLT,** with nut, washers and split pin. (For master or auxiliary rod). | | Histo |
| | | **CONNECTING ROD DETAILS.** | | |
| 30 A | 2 | Bearing, ball, master rod | Steel | Hitch |
| 1218 A | 9 | Bolt, gudgeon pin | Steel | Hiveb |
| 28 A | 8 | Bush, wrist pin | Phos. Bronze | Hivul |
| 1219 A | 9 | Nut, gudgeon pin bolt | Steel | Hoabe |
| 1160 A. 1 | 9 | Pin, gudgeon | Steel | Hoady |
| 1220 A | 9 | Pin, split, gudgeon pin bolt | Steel | Hoagu |
| 29 A. 1 | 8 | Pin, wrist, with stop | Steel | Hoard |
| 1446 A | 8 | Rod, auxiliary | Steel | Hoast |
| 2212 A | 1 | Rod, master, with 2 oil plugs driven in | Steel ⎫ * Steel ⎭ | Hoban |
| 1233 A | 8 | Screw, grub, wrist pin bush to auxiliary rod | Steel | Hobby |
| 1328 A | 18 | Washer, gudgeon pin bolt | Steel | Hobgo |
| | | **PISTON DETAILS.** | | |
| 2213 A | 9 | Piston body complete with 2 gudgeon pin bushes driven in and 2 stop screws riveted over | Aluminium ⎫ Phos. Bronze ⎬ * Steel ⎭ | Hobit |
| 1152 A. 1 | 9 | Ring, obturator, inner | Copper—Silver ⎫ | Hobna |
| 1153 A. 1 | 9 | Ring, obturator, outer | Copper—Silver ⎭ * | |
| 36 A. 1 | 27 | Ring, piston (cut), eccentric | C.I. | Hobox |
| 36 A. 2 | 27 | Ring, piston (cut), concentric | Hammered C.I. | Hobse |

The details listed above are illustrated on opposite page over their respective Part Nos.

* Supplied as one item.

# CLERGET 9B & 9BF PATENT AERO ENGINES.

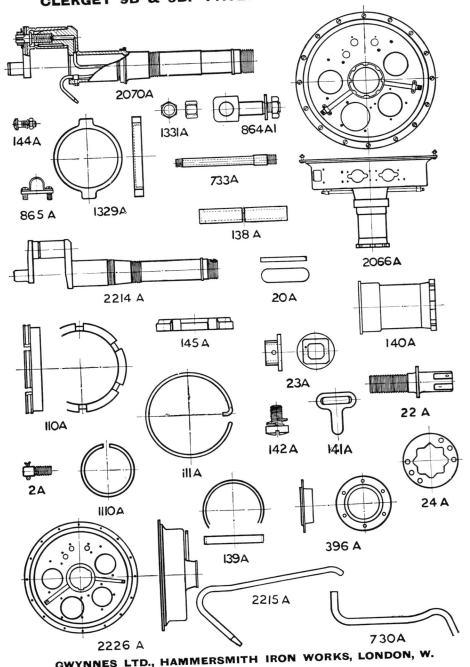

2070A

144A

1331A

864A1

733A

865 A

1329A

138 A

2066A

2214 A

20A

140A

145A

23A

110A

22 A

142A

141A

2A

111A

24 A

110A

139A

396 A

2215 A

2226 A

730A

GWYNNES LTD., HAMMERSMITH IRON WORKS, LONDON, W.

# CLERGET 9B & 9BF PATENT AERO ENGINES.

| Part No. | No. per Engine | Description | | Code-word for one. |
|---|---|---|---|---|
| 2070 A | 1 | **CRANKSHAFT,** short stroke, complete with maneton and key, maneton screw, nut, washer, studs and split pins, oil tube, petrol doping tube with nozzle, clamp, nut and washers and nut and locking ring for thrust, for engine 9B. | | Hobus |
| 2257 A | 1 | **CRANKSHAFT,** long stroke, with parts as above, for engine 9BF | | ‡ Hocir |
| 2066 A | 1 | **CENTRAL SUPPORT,** with oil connection and petrol doping connection soldered in, 2 clips with plates and screws, pair of half collars and containing sleeve, coupling nut to crankshaft, and 16 fixing bolts, nuts and spring washers. | | Hocka |
| 2226 A | 1 | **CENTRAL SUPPORT,** with studs for oil pump, air pump, and magneto, and 2 connections oil and petrol. | | Hocme |
| | | **CRANKSHAFT AND SUPPORT DETAILS.** | | |
| 144 A | 22 | Bolt, nut and washer, central or rear support | Steel | Hocus |
| 1329 A | 1 | Cap, dust, crankshaft | Brass | Hoddy |
| 1331 A | 1 | Cap, dust, pipe, doping | Brass | Hodge |
| 864 A. 1 | 1 | Clamp, doping tube, with nut and washer | Steel | Hodma |
| 865 A | 2 | Clip, oil or petrol connection, with plate and 2 screws | Brass clip ⎱ Steel plate ⎰ * and Screws | Hodom |
| 733 A | 2 | Connection, oil or petrol, to central support | Steel | Hoggo |
| 138 A | 1 | Collars, half, coupling nut, per pair | Steel | Hogin |
| 2214 A | 1 | Crankshaft, short stroke with maneton and key, engine 9B | Steel | Hogmy |
| 2258 A | 1 | Crankshaft, long stroke with maneton and key, engine 9BF | Steel | ‡ Hogok |
| 20 A | 2 | Key, central support to crankshaft | Steel | Hogsa |
| 140 A | 1 | Nut, coupling, central support to crankshaft | Steel | Hoisk |
| 110 A | 1 | Nut, crankshaft to thrust | Steel | Hoity |
| 145 A | 1 | Nut, rear support to crankshaft | Steel | Holin |
| 23 A | 1 | Nut, maneton screw to crankshaft | Steel | Holly |
| 111 A | 1 | Ring, locking, thrust nut to crankshaft | Steel | Holme |
| 1110 A | 1 | Ring, wire, ball bearing to maneton | Steel | Holot |
| 22 A | 1 | Screw, maneton to crankshaft | Steel | Holpo |
| 142 A | 1 | Screw, shaped washer to crankshaft, with spring washer | Steel | Holus |
| 139 A | 1 | Sleeve, sawn half collars | Steel | Holyd |
| 141 A | 1 | Stop, shaped, coupling nut | Steel | Homag |
| 24 A | 1 | Stop, shaped, maneton screw nut | Steel | Homby |
| 2 A | 2 | Stud, shaped washer, maneton, with split pin | Steel | Homca |
| 396 A | 1 | Support, rear | Steel | Homil |
| 730 A | 1 | Tube, oil, crankshaft | S.D. Copper | Hommo |
| 2215 A | 1 | Tube, petrol doping, crankshaft with nozzle | S.D. Copper ⎱ Brass ⎰ * | Homot |

The details listed above are illustrated on opposite page over their respective Part Nos. except items marked ‡

\* Supplied as one item.

3

# CLERGET 9B & 9BF PATENT AERO ENGINES.

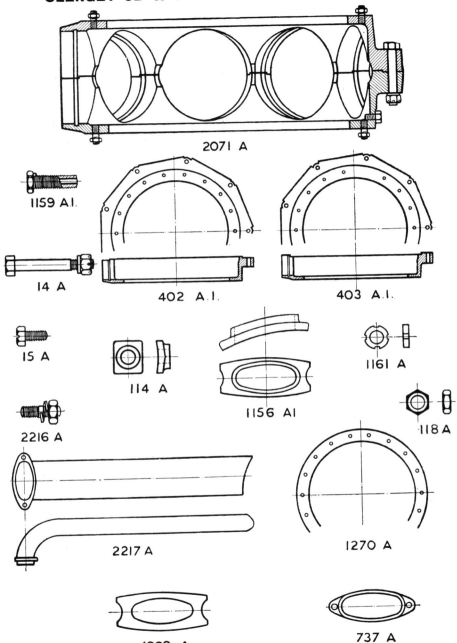

2071 A

1159 A1.

14 A

402 A.1.

403 A.1.

15 A

114 A

1156 A1

1161 A

118 A

2216 A

2217 A

1270 A

1269 A

737 A

GWYNNES LTD., HAMMERSMITH IRON WORKS, LONDON, W.

# CLERGET 9B & 9BF PATENT AERO ENGINES.

| Part No. | No. per Engine | Description | | Code-word for one. |
|---|---|---|---|---|
| 2071 A | 1 | **CRANK CASING,** complete with oil plug, 9 bolts, nuts, washers and split pins, and 36 studs, nuts and spring washers for attachment of distribution box and rear drum. | | Hompu |
| | | **CRANK CASING AND INDUCTION TUBE DETAILS.** | | |
| 1159 A. 1 | 9 | Bolt, clamp, tube flange to rear drum, with stop | Steel | Homun |
| 14 A | 9 | Bolt, nut, washer and split pin, crank casing assembling | Steel | Honat |
| 402 A. 1 | 1 | Casing, crank, front half | Steel | Honey |
| 403 A. 1 | 1 | Casing, crank, rear half | Steel | Hongs |
| 114 A | 9 | Clamp, tube flange to rear drum | Steel | Honif |
| 1156 A. 1 | 9 | Flange, tube to rear drum | Steel | Honna |
| 1161 A | 9 | Nut, fixing, clump bolt | Steel | Honor |
| 118 A | 18 | Nut, locking, clamp to rear drum | Steel | Honul |
| 15 A | 1 | Plug, oil, crank casing | Steel | Hooca |
| 2216 A | 36 | Stud, casing to distribution box or rear drum with nut and spring washer | Steel Steel Steel } * | Hoodi |
| 2217 A | 9 | Tube, induction, with flange to seat brazed on | Steel Steel } * | Hoofy |
| 1270 A | 2 | Washer, jointing, casing to distribution box or rear drum | Paper | Hooks |
| 1269 A | 9 | Washer, jointing, tube flange to rear drum | Fibre | Hoopu |
| 737 A | 9 | Washer, jointing, tube flange to valve seat | Copper— Asbestos | Hoosh |

The details listed above are illustrated on opposite page over their respective Part Nos.

*Supplied as one item.

# CLERGET 9B & 9BF PATENT AERO ENGINES.

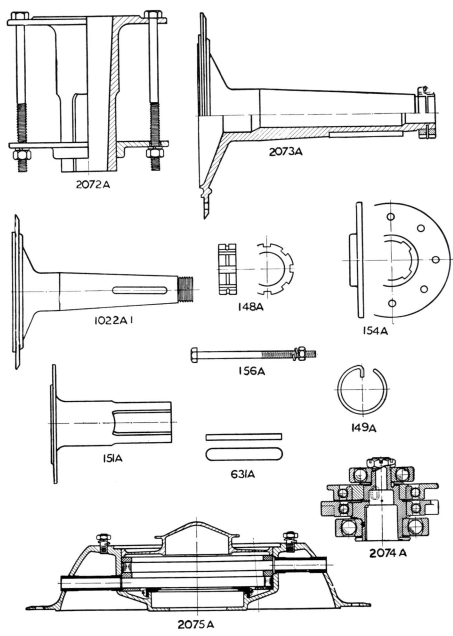

2072A

2073A

1022A1

148A

154A

156A

151A

149A

631A

2074 A

2075 A

GWYNNES LTD., HAMMERSMITH IRON WORKS, LONDON, W.

5

# CLERGET 9B & 9BF PATENT AERO ENGINES.

| Part No. | No. per Engine | Description | | Code-word for one. |
|---|---|---|---|---|
| 2072 A | 1 | **AIR SCREW HUB,** complete with flange and 8 bolts, with nuts and washers | | Hooth |
| 2073 A | 1 | **NOSE PIECE** (D. type), with nut, locking ring and key | | Hopan. |
| | | For combined nose-piece hub see page 10. | | |
| | | **HUB AND NOSE PIECE DETAILS.** | | |
| 156 A | 8 | Bolt, nut and washer, air screw hub | Steel | Hopba |
| 154 A | 1 | Flange, hub, air screw | Steel | Hopes |
| 151 A | 1 | Hub, air screw | Steel | Hopit |
| 631 A | 1 | Key, air screw hub to nose piece | Steel | Hopor |
| 1022 A | 1 | Nose piece, D Type | Steel | Hoppo |
| 148 A | 1 | Nut, air screw hub to nose piece | Steel | Horar |
| 149 A | 1 | Ring, locking, nose piece nut | Steel | Horbu |
| 2074 A | 1 | **EXTENSION SHAFT,** with front nut and split pin, front ball bearing, chamfered washer, exhaust eccentric with cam ball bearing and key, inlet cam ball bearing, rear ball bearing and rear nut with locking ring. | | Horco |
| 2075 A | 1 | **DISTRIBUTION BOX,** with 9 inlet tappet guides, 9 exhaust tappet guides, internal nut and locking ring for rear ball bearing, fixed disc, inlet gear ring with pegs, exhaust gear ring with pegs, gear ring key, centering plate, and studs, nuts and spring washers for nose piece, for engine 9BF | | Hordy |
| 2254 A | 1 | Ditto    ditto    ditto    for Engine 9B | | ‡Horeb |

The details listed above are illustrated on opposite page over their respective Part Nos. except item marked ‡

For details of extension shaft and distribution box, see next page.

# CLERGET 9B & 9BF PATENT AERO ENGINES.

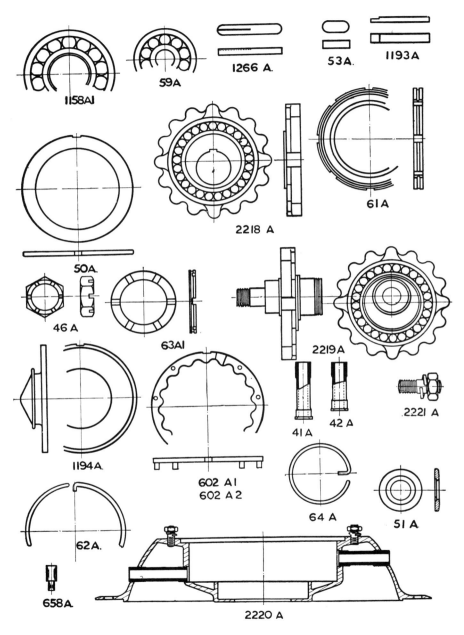

1158AI

59A

1266 A.

53A.

1193A

2218 A

61A

50A.

46 A

63AI

2219A

41A

42 A

.2221 A

1194A.

602 AI
602 A2

64 A

51 A

62A.

658A.

2220 A

## GWYNNES LTD., HAMMERSMITH IRON WORKS, LONDON, W.

# CLERGET 9B & 9BF PATENT AERO ENGINES.

| Part No. | No. per Engine | Description | | Code-word for one. |
|---|---|---|---|---|
| | | **EXTENSION SHAFT AND DISTRIBUTION BOX DETAILS.** | | |
| 59 A | 1 | Bearing, cam ball (see eccentric, also shaft) | | — |
| 1158 A. 1 | 1 | Bearing, ball, front, extension shaft | Steel | Horex |
| 2220 A | 1 | Bearing, ball, rear, extension shaft | Steel | Horiz |
| | | Box, distribution, engine 9BF | Steel | |
| | |     with exhaust tappet guides | Phos. Bronze | |
| | |     inlet tappet guides, and | Phos. Bronze | * Horla |
| | |     studs, nuts, and washers | Steel | |
| 2253 A | 1 | Ditto    ditto    for engine 9B | | ‡ Hormo |
| 50 A | 1 | Disc, fixed | Steel | Horne |
| 2218 A | 1 | Eccentric, exhaust, with | Steel | |
| | |     cam ball bearing riveted on | Steel } * | Horog |
| 42 A | 9 | Guide, exhaust tappet, engine 9BF | Phos. Bronze | Horpe |
| 1536 A | 9 |   ,,    ,,    ,,    ,,   9B | Phos. Bronze | ‡ Horst |
| 41 A | 9 | Guide, inlet tappet, engine 9BF | Phos. Bronze | Horth |
| 1535 A | 9 |   ,,    ,,    ,,    ,,   9B | Phos. Bronze | ‡ Horti |
| | | (See also box distribution for guides). | | |
| 53 A | 1 | Key, eccentric to extension shaft | Steel | Horup |
| 1193 A | 1 | Key, gear rings to distribution box | Steel | Hosan |
| 1266 A | 1 | Key, shaft, extension to maneton | Steel | Hosca |
| 61 A | 1 | Nut, bearing, rear to distribution box | Steel | Hosel |
| 63 A. 1 | 1 | Nut, bearing, rear to extension shaft | Steel | Hosie |
| 46 A | 1 | Nut and split pin, front, extension shaft | Steel | Hosky |
| 658 A | 16 | Peg, distance, see also ring, gear | Steel | Hosod |
| 1194 A | 1 | Plate, centering, front bearing | Steel | Hospo |
| 602 A. 2 | 1 | Ring, gear, exhaust, with distance pegs | Steel | Hosti |
| 602 A. 1 | 1 | Ring, gear, inlet, with distance pegs | Steel | Hosud |
| 62 A | 1 | Ring, locking, nut, rear bearing to distribution box | Steel | Hotas |
| 64 A | 1 | Ring, locking, rear nut to extension shaft | Steel | Hotch |
| 2219 A | 1 | Shaft, extension, with | Steel } * | |
| | |     cam ball bearing riveted on | Steel | Hotep |
| 2221 A | 14 | Stud, nut and spring washer, nose piece to distribution box | Steel | Hotmo |
| 51 A | 1 | Washer, chamfered, front bearing to eccentric | Steel | Hound |

The details listed above are illustrated on opposite page over their respective Part Nos.
except those marked ‡

* Supplied as one item.

# CLERGET 9B & 9BF PATENT AERO ENGINES.

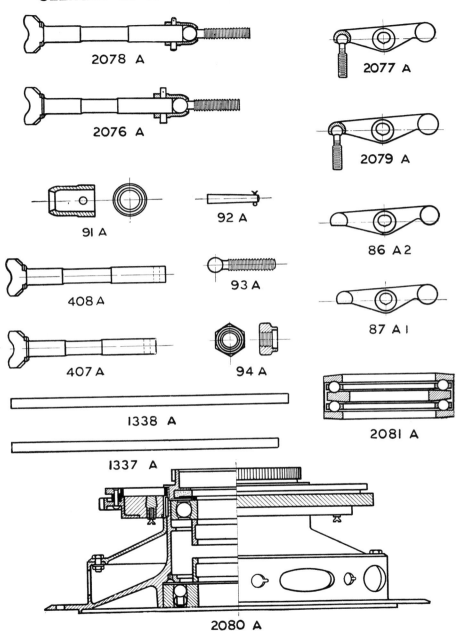

2078 A

2076 A

91 A

92 A

408 A

93 A

407 A

94 A

1338 A

1337 A

2080 A

2077 A

2079 A

86 A 2

87 A 1

2081 A

**GWYNNES LTD., HAMMERSMITH IRON WORKS, LONDON, W.**

# CLERGET 9B & 9BF PATENT AERO ENGINES.

| Part No. | No. per Engine | Description | | Code word for one. |
|---|---|---|---|---|
| 2076 A | 9 | **EXHAUST TAPPET,** with ball cap, taper pin with split pin, and ball-ended screw, engine 9BF | | Hours |
| 2256 A | 9 | Ditto ditto for ,, 9B | | ‡ Houst |
| 2077 A | 9 | **EXHAUST ROCKING LEVER,** with ball-ended screw riveted in, for engine 9BF | | Hovel |
| 2259 A | 9 | Ditto ditto ,, ,, 9B | | ‡ Hovga |
| 2078 A | 9 | **INLET TAPPET,** with ball cap, taper pin with split pin, and ball-ended screw, engine 9BF | | Hovis |
| 2255 A | 9 | Ditto ditto for ,, 9B | | ‡ Hovon |
| 2079 A | 9 | **INLET ROCKING LEVER,** with ball-ended screw riveted in, for engine 9BF | | Howit |
| 2260 A | 9 | Ditto ditto ,, ,, 9B | | ‡ Howka |
| | | **TAPPET AND LEVER GEAR DETAILS.** | | |
| 91 A | 18 | Cap, ball, tappet, exhaust or inlet, 9BF | Steel | Howls |
| 1537 A | 18 | " " " " " 9B | Steel | ‡ Howop |
| 87 A. 1 | 9 | Lever, rocking, exhaust, 9BF | Steel | Hucks |
| 87 A | 9 | " " " 9B | Steel | ‡ Hucmi |
| 86 A. 2 | 9 | Lever, rocking, inlet, 9BF | Steel | Hufat |
| 86 A. 1 | 9 | " " ,, 9B | Steel | ‡ Hufer |
| 94 A | 36 | Nut, back, push rod | Steel | Huffy |
| 92 A | 18 | Pin, taper, ball cap, with split pin | Steel | Hugas |
| 1338 A | 9 | Rod, push, exhaust (tube) | Steel | Hulky |
| 1337 A | 9 | Rod, push, inlet (tube) | Steel | Hulla |
| 93 A | 36 | Screw, ball-ended, exhaust or inlet | Steel | Human |
| 407 A | 9 | Tappet, exhaust, 9BF | Steel | Humel |
| 1528 A | 9 | " " 9B | Steel | ‡ Humgo |
| 408 A | 9 | Tappet, inlet, 9BF | Steel | Humid |
| 1527 A | 9 | " ,, 9B | Steel | ‡ Humke |
| 2080 A | 1 | **REAR DRUM,** with front ball bearing, rear ball bearing, front nut with fixing screw, front and rear distance piece, rear distance washer, oil retaining washer, main driving wheel, distributor with distance piece, gun cam, rear drum cover, and 18 bolts, cover to rear drum with nuts and spring washers. | | Humme |
| 2081 A | 1 | **DOUBLE THRUST BEARING,** comprising one central race, two outer races, two ball cages with balls and one central distance piece. | | Humor |

The details listed above are illustrated on opposite page over their respective Part Nos., except items marked ‡

For details of rear drum and thrust gear see next page.

# CLERGET 9B & 9BF PATENT AERO ENGINES.

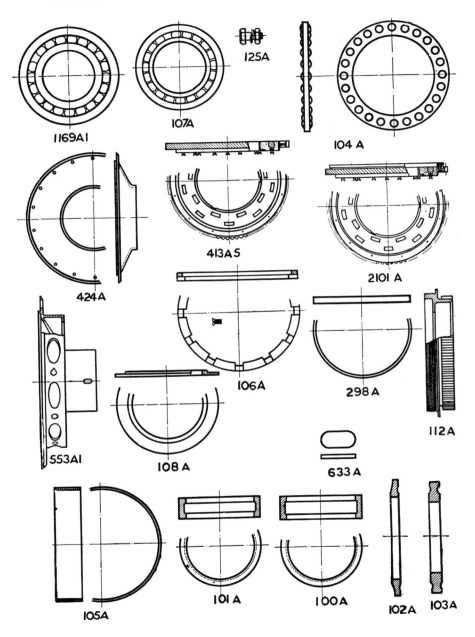

125A

1169AI

107A

104 A

424A

413A5

2101 A

553AI

106A

298A

112A

108 A

633 A

105A

101 A

100A

102A

103A

GWYNNES LTD., HAMMERSMITH IRON WORKS, LONDON, W.

# CLERGET 9B & 9BF PATENT AERO ENGINES.

| Part No. | No. per Engine | Description | | Code-word for one. |
|---|---|---|---|---|
| | | **REAR DRUM AND THRUST GEAR DETAILS.** | | |
| 1169 A. 1 | 1 | Bearing ball, main, front | Steel | Humps |
| 107 A | 1 | Bearing ball, rear | Steel | Humso |
| 125 A | 18 | Bolt, cover to rear drum, with nut and spring washer | Steel | Humus |
| 104 A | 2 | Cage ball, with balls | | Hunch |
| 424 A | 1 | Cover, rear drum | Steel | Hunga |
| 413 A. 5 | 1 | Distributor, 18 point, drilled for gun interrupter cam, but without cam | | Hunke |
| 2101 A | 1 | Distributor, 18 point with interrupter cam riveted on | | Hunts |
| 553 A. 1 | 1 | Drum, rear | Steel | Hurax |
| 633 A | 2 | Key, distributor to rear drum | Steel | Hurds |
| 106 A | 1 | Nut, thrust to rear drum, with fixing screw | Steel | Huren |
| 298 A | 1 | Piece, distance, distributor to driving wheel | Steel | Hurka |
| 105 A | 1 | Piece, distance, thrust, central (thin) | Steel | Hurlo |
| 101 A | 1 | Piece, distance, thrust, front (short) | Steel | Hurry |
| 100 A | 1 | Piece, distance, thrust, rear (long) | Steel | Hursk |
| 103 A | 1 | Race, thrust, central | Steel | Hurti |
| 102 A | 2 | Race, thrust, outer | Steel | Hurve |
| 108 A | 1 | Washer, distance, rear bearing to oil retaining washer | Steel | Husba |
| 109 A | 1 | Washer, oil retaining | ‡ Leather | Husks |
| 112 A | 1 | Wheel, driving, main | Steel | Husmo |

The details listed above are illustrated on opposite page over their respective Part Nos., except item marked ‡

# CLERGET 9B & 9BF PATENT AERO ENGINES.

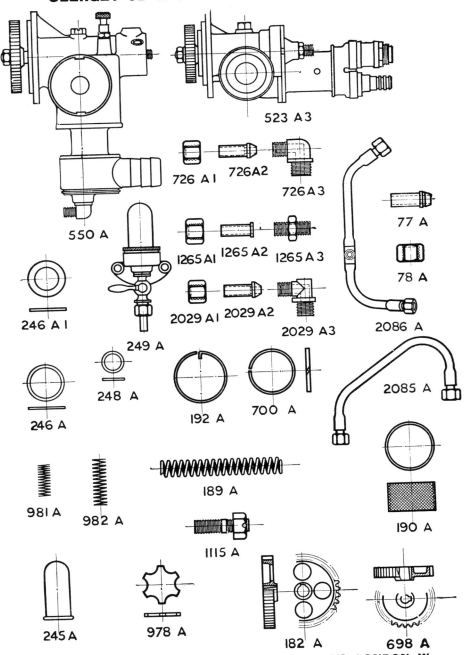

523 A3

726 A I   726A2

726A3

550 A

77 A

1265A1   1265 A2   1265 A 3

78 A

2029 A1   2029 A2

2029 A3

2086 A

246 A I

249 A

248 A

2085 A

246 A

192 A

700 A

189 A

981 A

982 A

190 A

1115 A

245 A

978 A

182 A

698 A

# CLERGET 9B & 9BF PATENT AERO ENGINES.

| Part No. | No. per Engine | Description | | Code-word for one. |
|---|---|---|---|---|
| 550 A | 1 | **OIL PUMP,** with pinion | | Hussa |
| 523 A. 3 | 1 | **AIR PUMP,** with pinion | | Husty |
| 249 A | 1 | **PULSATOR,** complete | | Hutme |
| | | **OIL AND AIR PUMP AND PULSATOR DETAILS.** | | |
| 78 A | 1 | Nut union, main oil pipe, engine end | Steel | Huxle |
| 726 A. 1 | 1 | Nut, union, main oil pipe, pump end. | Brass | Huzza |
| 1265 A. 1 | 2 | Nut, union, oil to air pump, air pump end, or drain | Brass | Hyact |
| 2029 A. 1 | 1 | Nut, union, oil to air pump, oil pump end | Brass | Hyade |
| 77 A | 1 | Nipple, main oil pipe, engine end | Steel | Hybod |
| 726 A. 2 | 1 | Nipple, main oil pipe, oil pump end | Brass | Hybry |
| 1265 A. 2 | 2 | Nipple, oil to air pump, air pump end or drain | Brass | Hyalo |
| 2029 A.2 | 1 | Nipple, oil to air pump, oil pump end | Brass | Hyber |
| 182 A | 1 | Pinion, oil pump | Steel | Hydat |
| 698 A | 1 | Pinion, air pump | Steel | Hydro |
| 2085 A | 1 | Pipe, oil, air pump supply, with nipples and nuts | Copper | Hyena |
| 2086 A | 1 | Pipe, oil, main, with nipples and nuts | Copper | Hyest |
| 246 A | 1 | Ring, joint, upper, air vessel, pulsator | Leather | Hylic |
| 246 A. 1 | 1 | Ring, joint, lower, air vessel, pulsator | Leather | Hylke |
| 248 A | 1 | Ring, joint, oil cock, pulsator | Leather | Hylla |
| 192 A | 1 | Ring, locking, nut, oil pump suction box | Steel | Hygra |
| 700 A | 2 | Ring, plunger, air pump | Phos. Bronze | Hylar |
| 190 A | 1 | Strainer, oil | Brass | Hylop |
| 981 A | 1 | Spring, air pump, delivery | Steel | Hylus |
| 982 A | 1 | Spring, air pump, relief | Steel | Hymac |
| 189 A | 2 | Spring, oil pump | Steel | Hymen |
| 1115 A | 4 | Stud, oil pump barrel to gear case with nut and split pin | Steel | Hymod |
| 726 A. 3 | 1 | Union, angled, main oil pipe, oil pump end | G.M. | Hymno |
| 2029 A. 3 | 1 | Union, angled, oil to air pump, oil pump end | G.M. | Hyoid |
| 1265 A. 3 | 2 | Union, straight, oil to air pump, air pump end or drain | Brass | Hypat |
| 978 A | 2 | Valve, air pump, delivery or relief | Steel | Hyper |
| 245 A | 1 | Vessel, air, pulsator | Glass | Hypic |

The details listed above are illustrated on opposite page over their respective Part Nos.

# CLERGET 9B & 9BF PATENT AERO ENGINES.

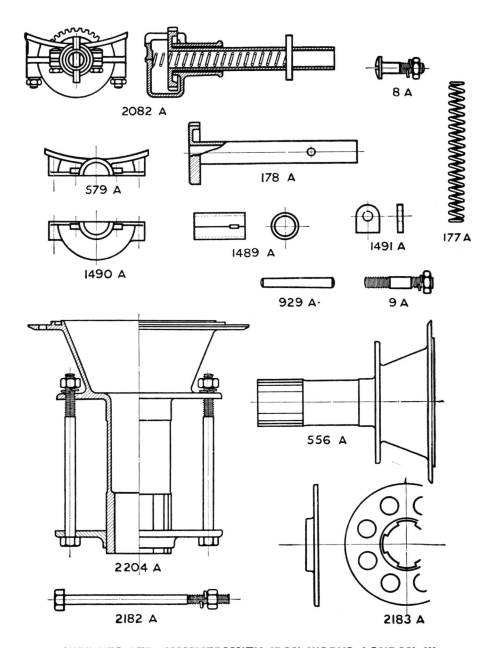

2082 A

8 A

178 A

579 A

1489 A

1491 A

177 A

1490 A

929 A·

9 A

2204 A

556 A

2182 A

2183 A

**GWYNNES LTD., HAMMERSMITH IRON WORKS, LONDON, W.**

# CLERGET 9B & 9BF PATENT AERO ENGINES.

| Part No. | No. per Engine | Description | | Code-word for one. |
|---|---|---|---|---|
| 2082 A | 1 | **HAND STARTER,** comprising pinion, case and cap bearing bush and locking plates, spring and taper stop pin, assembly bolts and studs, with nuts and spring washers | | Hypos |
| 2204 A | 1 | **COMBINED NOSE-PIECE HUB,** comprising nose-piece hub, air screw plate and air screw bolts with nuts and spring washers | | Hypsa |
| | | **STARTER AND COMBINED NOSE-PIECE HUB DETAILS.** | | |
| 2183 A | 8 | Bolt, air screw, with nut and spring washer | Steel | Hypti |
| 8 A | 2 | Bolt, assembly, starter, with nut and spring washer | Steel | Hypul |
| 1489 A | 1 | Bush, starter casing, in halves | G.M. | Hyrac |
| 1490 A | 1 | Cap, starter casing | Aluminium | Hyste |
| 579 A | 1 | Casing, starter | Aluminium | Hythe |
| 556 A | 1 | Nose-piece hub, combined | Steel | Hyvon |
| 929 A | 1 | Pin, taper, forming spring stop | Steel | Iatur |
| 178 A | 1 | Pinion, starter, helical teeth | Steel | Iceho |
| 2182 A | 1 | Plate, air screw | Steel | Iceku |
| 1491 A | 2 | Plate, locking, casing bush | G.M. | Icela |
| 177 A | 1 | Spring, starter, spiral | Steel | Ichor |
| 9 A | 2 | Stud, assembly, starter, with nut and spring washer | Steel | Icing |

The details listed above are illustrated on opposite page over their respective Part Nos.

# CLERGET 9B & 9BF PATENT AERO ENGINES.

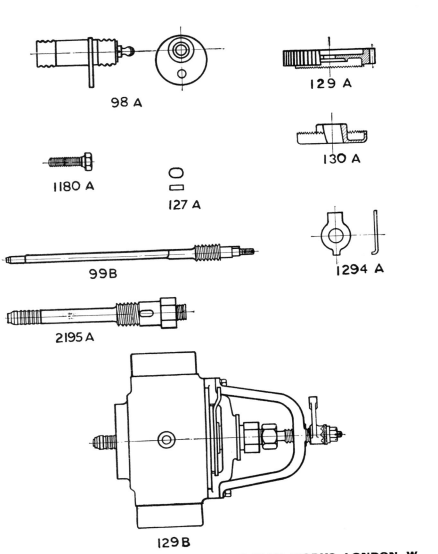

320 A

738 A I

98 A

129 A

130 A

1180 A

127 A

99B

1294 A

2195 A

129 B

**GWYNNES LTD., HAMMERSMITH IRON WORKS, LONDON, W.**

# CLERGET 9B & 9BF PATENT AERO ENGINES.

| Part No. | No. per Engine | Description | | | Code-word for one. |
|---|---|---|---|---|---|
| | | **IGNITION DETAILS.** | | | |
| 320 A | 3 | Brush, carbon, with spring | | | Icono |
| 738 A. 1 | 2 | Connector, H.T. magneto to brush holder | | | Icosa |
| 98 A | 3 | Holder, brush | | | Icter |
| 130 A | 2 | Hub, crown, magneto pinion | Steel | | Ictus |
| 127 A | 2 | Key, pinion hub to magneto spindle | Steel | | Ideas |
| 1588 A | 2 | Magneto, running (A.D.S.) | | ‡ | Ident |
| 1517 A | 1 | Magneto, starting (P.L.H.) | | ‡ | Idial |
| 129 A | 2 | Pinion, magneto | Steel | | Idice |
| 1496 A | 18 | Plug, sparking (K.L.G.) | | ‡ | Idiot |
| 1180 A | 2 | Screw, fixing, pinion to magneto spindle | Steel | | Idlap |
| 1294 A | 2 | Washer, locking, pinion fixing screw | Copper | | Idler |
| 741 A | 18 | Washer, sparking plug | Copper—Asbestos | ‡ | Idols |
| 739 A. 1 | 18 | Wire, distributor end | Soft Brass | ‡ | Idria |
| 739 A. 2 | 18 | Wire, sparking plug end | Soft Brass | ‡ | Iduna |
| | | **CARBURETTOR.** | | | |
| 129 B | 1 | Carburettor, complete | | | Idule |
| 2195 A | 1 | Jet, carburettor, with nozzle and two keys | Bronze Steel | } | Iduro |
| 99 B | 1 | Needle, carburettor | Bronze | | Idust |

The details listed above are illustrated on opposite page over their respective Part Nos. except items marked ‡

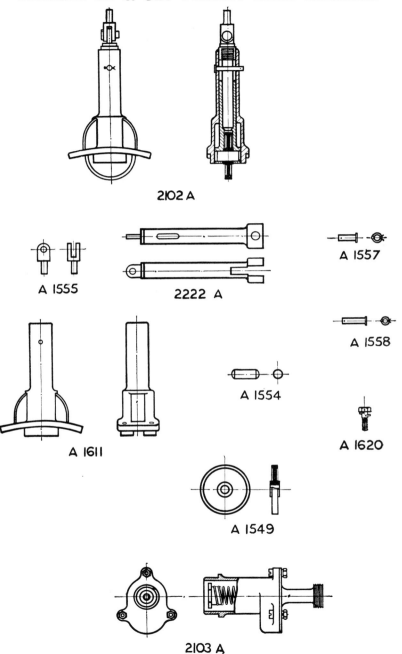

2102 A

A 1555

2222 A

A 1557

A 1558

A 1554

A 1611

A 1620

A 1549

2103 A

GWYNNES LTD., HAMMERSMITH IRON WORKS, LONDON, W.

12

# CLERGET 9B & 9BF PATENT AERO ENGINES.

| Part No. | No. per Engine | Description | | Code-word for one. |
|---|---|---|---|---|
| 2102 A | 2 | **GUN INTERRUPTER TAPPET ASSEMBLY,** comprising push rod and guide, roller and pin, guide pin, fork end and pin | | Idyll |
| | | **GUN INTERRUPTER TAPPET DETAILS.** | | |
| A-1555 | 2 | Fork, operation rod | Steel | Ignat |
| A-1611 | 2 | Guide, push rod | Man. Bronze | Igneo |
| A-1557 | 2 | Pin, fork, operating rod | Steel | Ignif |
| A-1558 | 2 | Pin, guide, push rod, with split pin | Steel | Ignob |
| A-1554 | 2 | Pin, roller, push rod | Steel | Igoat |
| 2222 A | 2 | Rod, push, interrupter, with eye piece | Steel | Igose |
| A-1549 | 2 | Roller, push rod | Steel | Ileam |
| A-1620 | 8 | Screw, guide, push-rod assembly with spring washer | Steel | Ileus |
| 2103 A | 1 | **SPEEDOMETER DRIVE GEAR BOX,** complete with flexible connector to oil pump shaft | | Iliac |

The details listed above are illustrated on opposite page over their respective Part Nos.

# CLERGET 9B & 9BF PATENT AERO ENGINES.

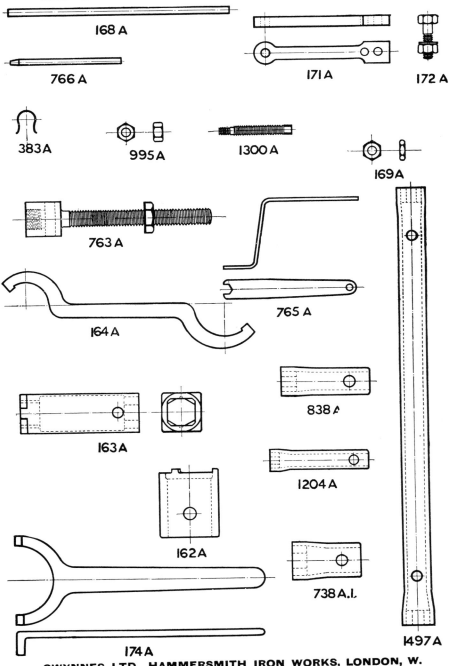

168 A

766 A

171 A

172 A

383 A

995 A

1300 A

169 A

763 A

765 A

164 A

838 A

163 A

1204 A

162 A

738 A.l.

174 A

1497 A

GWYNNES LTD., HAMMERSMITH IRON WORKS, LONDON, W.

## CLERGET 9B & 9BF PATENT AERO ENGINES.

| Part No. | No. per Engine | Description | Code-word for one. |
|---|---|---|---|
| 2104 A | 1 | **TOOL KIT,** comprising set of tools for one engine to the following list packed in polished case with two trays, padlock, handles, brass hinges and stop for lid, and name plates for all tools. | Ilide |
| | | **TOOL DETAILS.** | |
| 168 A | 1 | Bar, tommy, large | Ilift |
| 766 A | 1 | Bar, tommy, small | Ilimp |
| 172 A | 1 | Bolt, tightener, lever bracket, with nut and washer | Ilink |
| 383 A | 18 | Clip, tappet | Ilips |
| 799 A | 1 | Drift, key | ‡ Ilish |
| 171 A | 1 | Link, tightener, lever bracket | Illap |
| 995 A | 1 | Nut, drawing screw, wrist pin | Illco |
| 169 A | 1 | Nut, standard 167A, thrust and distribution box plate spanners | Illeg |
| 772 A | 1 | Pliers, for split pins | ‡ Illga |
| 1300 A | 1 | Screw, drawing, wrist pins | Illit |
| 763 A | 1 | Screw, withdrawing, distribution box, with nut | Illna |
| 771 A | 1 | Screwdriver, large | ‡ Illos |
| 794 A | 1 | Screwdriver, small | ‡ Illty |
| 765 A | 1 | Spanner, bent, single ended, 10.6m/m over flats, nut for bolt, cover and rear drum | Illud |
| 1497 A | 1 | Spanner, box, double ended, clamp bolt | Imact |
| 163 A | 1 | Spanner, box, double ended, extension shaft and maneton | Imady |
| 162 A | 1 | Spanner, box, single ended, bearing, rear to distribution box | Image |
| 838 A | 1 | Spanner, box, single ended, casing bolt | Imath |
| 1204 A | 1 | Spanner, box, single ended, nuts fixing distribution box and rear drum | Imban |
| 768 A. 1 | 1 | Spanner, box, single ended, sparking plug | Imbel |
| 164 A | 1 | Spanner, claw, double ended, castle nuts | Imbic |
| 174 A | 1 | Spanner, claw, single ended, nut, thrust to crankshaft | Imbos |

The details listed above are illustrated on opposite page over their respective Part Nos. except items marked ‡

# CLERGET 9B & 9BF PATENT AERO ENGINES.

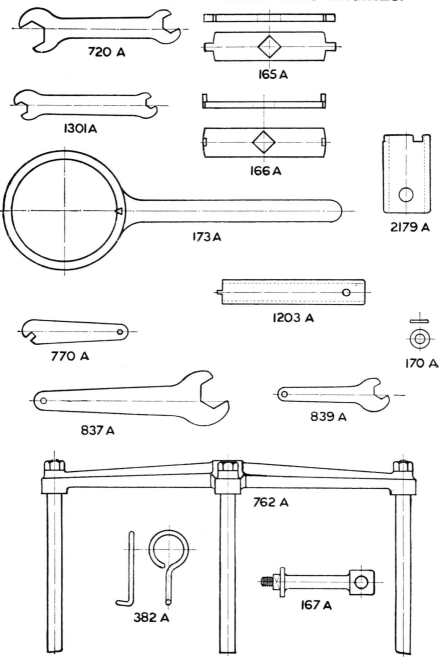

720 A

165 A

1301A

166 A

2179 A

173 A

1203 A

170 A

770 A

837 A

839 A

762 A

382 A

167 A

**GWYNNES LTD., HAMMERSMITH IRON WORKS, LONDON, W.**

# CLERGET 9B & 9BF PATENT AERO ENGINES.

| Part No. | No. per Engine | Description | Code-word for one. |
|---|---|---|---|
| | | **TOOL DETAILS (CONTINUED).** | |
| 720 A | 1 | Spanner, double ended, 26m/m and 17·6m/m hex. over flats, air pump | Imbra |
| 1301 A | 1 | Spanner, double ended, 14m/m and 10·6m/m hex. over flats, magneto and support bolts | Imbue |
| 165 A | 1 | Spanner, plate, bearing thrust to rear drum ; used with standard 167A | Imear |
| 166 A | 1 | Spanner, plate, bearing rear to extension shaft ; used with standard 167A | Imeco |
| 173 A | 1 | Spanner, ring, single ended, main driving wheel | Imend |
| 770 A | 1 | Spanner, single ended, holding, for ball-ended screws | Imice |
| 837 A | 1 | Spanner, single ended, 28·2m/m hex. over flats, withdrawing distribution box | Imilk |
| 839 A | 1 | Spanner, single ended, 14m/m hex. over flats, nut, push rod | Imint |
| 1203 A | 1 | Spanner, tube, single ended, nut, fixing clamp bolt | Imish |
| 2179 A | 1 | Spanner, tube, single ended, seat, exhaust valve, Type A or B | Imita |
| 167 A | 1 | Standard, thrust plate spanner 165A and bearing plate spanner 166A | Imixy |
| 382 A | 2 | Tool, hook, drawing cam gear | Immac |
| 762 A | 1 | Tripod, withdrawing distribution box | Immes |
| 170 A | 1 | Washer, standard 167A | Immig |

The details listed above are illustrated on opposite page over their respective Part Nos.

# CLERGET 9B & 9BF PATENT AERO ENGINES.

| Part No. | No. per Engine | Description | Dia. | Long | Code-word for one. |
|---|---|---|---|---|---|
| | | **SCREWS, STUDS AND BOLTS.** | | | |
| 1467 A | 3 | Screw, brush holder to support | 6m/m | 10m/m | Immus |
| 125 A | 18 | Bolt and nut, cover to rear drum | 6m/m | 12m/m | Imona |
| 1285 A | 18 | Screw, flange to inlet seat | 6m/m | 14m/m | Imoby |
| 144 A | 16 | Bolt and nut, central support | 6m/m | 18m/m | Imoce |
| 144 A | 6 | Bolt and nut, rear support | 6m/m | 18m/m | Imoce |
| 8 A | 2 | Bolt and nut, starter casing assembly | 6m/m | 22m/m | Imods |
| 270 A | 4 | Stud and nut, air pump to support | 6m/m | 23m/m | Imoft |
| 10 A | 4 | Bolt and nut, starter to support | 7m/m | 18m/m | Imogg |
| 3 A | 6 | Stud, magneto to support | 8m/m | 15m/m | Imoil |
| 3 A | 4 | Stud, oil pump to support | 8m/m | 15m/m | Imoil |
| 2216 A | 36 | Stud and nut, crankcase | 8m/m | 25m/m | Imorc |
| 2221 A | 14 | Stud and nut, nose piece to distribution box | 8m/m | 25m/m | Imord |
| 9 A | 2 | Stud and nut, starter casing assembly | 8m/m | 48m/m | Imosa |
| 14 A | 9 | Bolt and nut, with flat washer and split pin, crankcase assembly | 11m/m | 97m/m | Imoth |
| | | **SPRING WASHERS.** | | | |
| 2105 A | | Suitable for 5m/m bolt | | | Imour |
| 2106 A | | Suitable for 6m/m bolt | | | Imova |
| 2107 A | | Suitable for 7m/m bolt | | | Impas |
| 2108 A | | Suitable for 8m/m bolt | | | Impca |

# PART NUMBER INDEX.

PART NUMBER INDEX—(Continued).

| Part No. | Page | Part No. | Page | Part No. | Page | Part No. | Page |
|----------|------|----------|------|----------|------|----------|------|
| 1265A3 | 9 | 1537A | 7 | 2085A | 9 | 2217A | 4 |
| 1266A | 6 | 1588A | 11 | 2086A | 9 | 2218A | 6 |
| 1269A | 4 | 1599A | 1 | 2099A | 1 | 2219A | 6 |
| 1270A | 4 | 2029A1 | 9 | 2100A | 1 | 2220A | 6 |
| 1285A | 1,15 | 2029A2 | 9 | 2101A | 8 | 2221A | 6, 15 |
| 1294A | 11 | 2029A3 | 9 | 2102A | 12 | 2222A | 12 |
| 1300A | 13 | 2036A | 1 | 2103A | 12 | 2226A | 3 |
| 1301A | 14 | 2037A1 | 1 | 2104A | 13 | 2227A | 1 |
| 1328A | 2 | 2063A | 1 | 2105A | 15 | 2253A | 6 |
| 1329A | 3 | 2064A | 1 | 2106A | 15 | 2254A | 5 |
| 1331A | 3 | 2065A | 1 | 2107A | 15 | 2255A | 7 |
| 1331A | 3 | 2066A | 3 | 2108A | 15 | 2256A | 7 |
| 1335A | 1 | 2067A | 2 | 2174A | 1 | 2257A | 3 |
| 1336A | 1 | 2068A | 2 | 2175A | 1 | 2258A | 3 |
| 1337A | 7 | 2069A | 2 | 2179A | 14 | 2259A | 7 |
| 1338A | 7 | 2070A | 3 | 2182A | 10 | 2260A | 7 |
| 1446A | 2 | 2071A | 4 | 2183A | 10 | 99B | 11 |
| 1467A | 15 | 2072A | 5 | 2185A | 1 | 129B | 11 |
| 1489A | 10 | 2073A | 5 | 2195A | 11 | A–1549 | 12 |
| 1490A | 10 | 2074A | 5 | 2204A | 10 | A–1554 | 12 |
| 1491A | 10 | 2075A | 5 | 2208A | 1 | A–1555 | 12 |
| 1496A | 11 | 2076A | 7 | 2209A | 1 | A–1557 | 12 |
| 1497A | 13 | 2077A | 7 | 2211A | 1 | A–1558 | 12 |
| 1517A | 11 | 2078A | 7 | 2212A | 2 | A–1611 | 12 |
| 1527A | 7 | 2079A | 7 | 2213A | 2 | A–1620 | 12 |
| 1528A | 7 | 2080A | 7 | 2214A | 3 | | |
| 1535A | 6 | 2081A | 7 | 2215A | 3 | | |
| 1536A | 6 | 2082A | 10 | 2216A | 4, 15 | | |

Frost & Sons,
Printers, Rugby

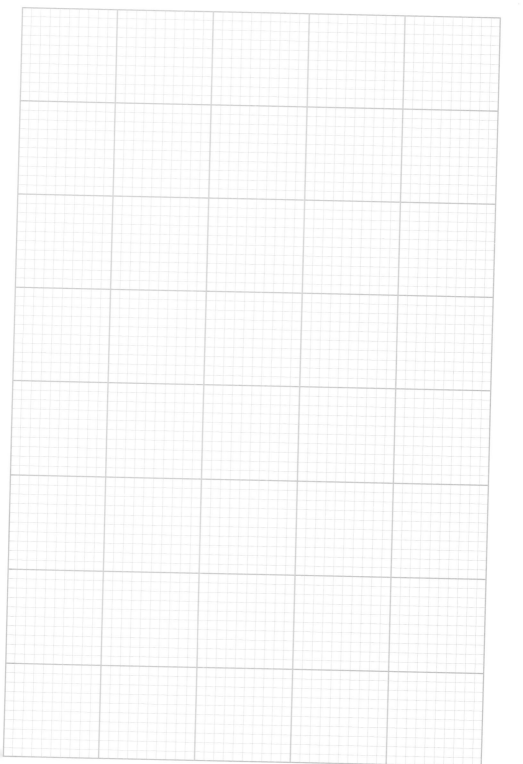

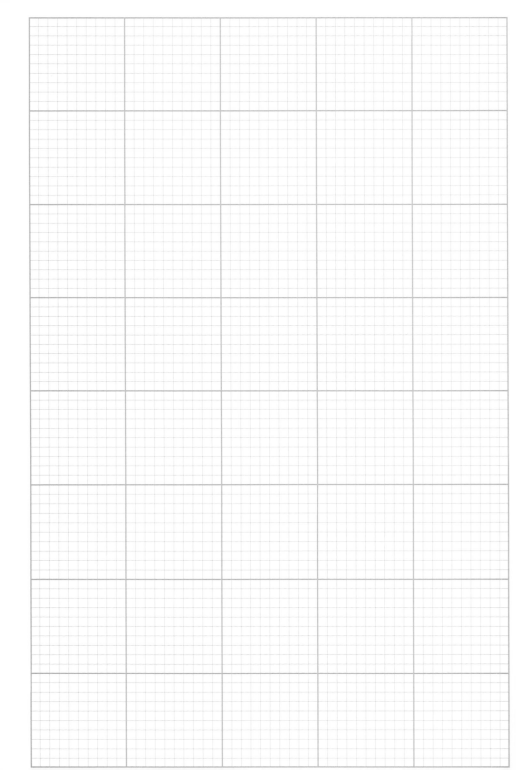

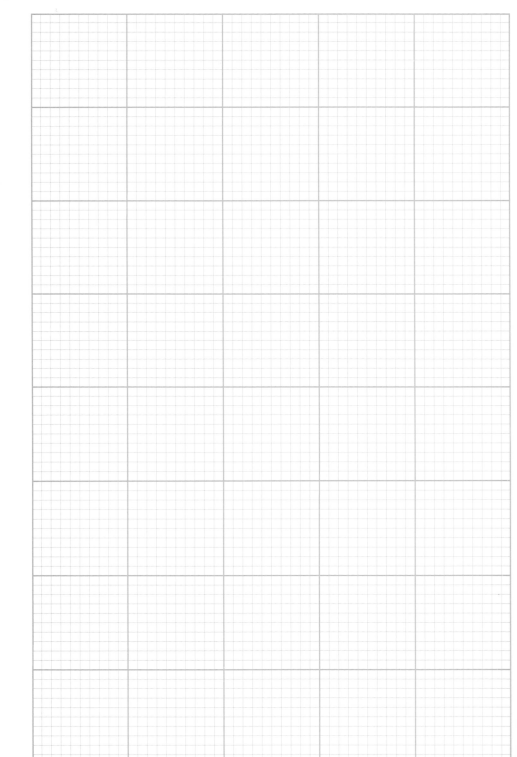

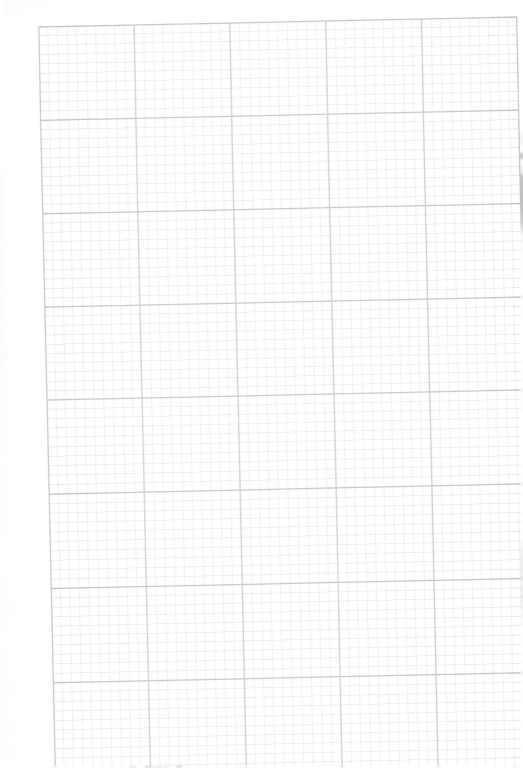